MAD TALES FROM

THE RAJ

Petro suo,
ð.ð. Simon RT.
ααϫα Aug. 1995.

THE WELLCOME INSTITUTE SERIES IN THE HISTORY OF MEDICINE

Edited by W.F. Bynum and Roy Porter
The Wellcome Institute

Medical Fringe and Medical Orthodoxy 1750–1850
W.F. Bynum and Roy Porter

Florence Nightingale and the Nursing Legacy
Monica Baly

Social Hygiene in Twentieth Century Britain
Greta Jones

Problems and Methods in the History of Medicine
Roy Porter and Andrew Wear

Vivisection in Historical Perspective
Nicolaas A. Rupke

Abortion in England, 1900–1967
Barbara Brookes

The Hospital in History
Edited by Lindsay Granshaw and Roy Porter

Women as Mothers in Pre-industrial England
Edited by Valerie Fildes

Birth Control in Germany, 1871–1933
James Woycke

The Charitable Imperative
Colin Jones

Medicine at the Courts of Europe, 1500–1837
Edited by Dr Vivian Nutton

MAD TALES FROM THE RAJ

THE EUROPEAN INSANE IN BRITISH INDIA, 1800–1858

Waltraud Ernst

London and New York

Für meine Eltern

First published in 1991
by Routledge
11 New Fetter Lane, London EC4P 4EE

Simultaneously published in the USA and Canada
by Routledge
a division of Routledge, Chapman and Hall Inc.
29 West 35th Street, New York, NY 10001

Typeset by LaserScript Limited, Mitcham, Surrey
Printed in Great Britain by Biddles Ltd,
Guildford and King's Lynn

British Library Cataloguing in Publication Data
Ernst, Waltraud *1955–*
Mad tales from the Raj: the European Insane in British
India, 1800–1858. – (The Wellcome Institute series in the
history of medicine)
1. India. Medicine. Social aspects, history
I. Title II. Series
362.10420954

Library of Congress Cataloging in Publication Data
Ernst, Waltraud, 1955–
Mad tales from the Raj: the European insane in British India,
1800–1858/by Waltraud Ernst.
p. cm. – (The Wellcome Institute series in the history of
medicine)
Includes bibliographical references.
1. Psychiatry – India – History. 2. British – Mental health – India –
History.
3. Psychiatry – Great Britain – History. 4. India – History – British
occupation, 1765–1947. I. Title. II. Series.
RC451.I4E76 1990
616.89'00954'09034 – dc20   90-8521

ISBN 0-415-00940-5

Thrown away

And some are sulky, while some will plunge.
[*So ho! Steady! Stand still, you!*]
Some you must gentle, and some you must lunge.
[*There! There! Who wants to kill you?*]
Some – there are losses in every trade –
Will break their hearts ere bitted and made,
Will fight like fiends as the rope cuts hard,
And die dumb-mad in the breaking-yard.
                    Toolungala Stockyard Chorus

. . . Now India is a place beyond all others where one must
not take things too seriously – the mid-day sun always ex-
cepted. . . .

But [a] Boy – the tale is as old as the Hills – came out, and
took all things seriously. He was pretty and was petted. He took
the pettings seriously, and fretted over women not worth
saddling a pony to call upon. He found his new free life in India
very good. It does look attractive in the beginning, from a
subaltern's point of view – all ponies, partners, dancing, and so
on. He tasted it as the puppy tastes the soap. Only he came late
to the eating, with a grown set of teeth. He had no sense of
balance – just like the puppy – and could not understand why
he was not treated with the consideration he received under his
father's roof. This hurt his feelings.

He quarrelled with other boys and, being sensitive to the
marrow, remembered these quarrels, and they excited him. He
found whist, and gymkhanas, and things of that kind (meant to
amuse one after office) good; but he took them seriously too,

v

just as seriously as he took the 'head' that followed after drink. He lost his money over whist and gymkhanas because they were new to him. . . .

This unbridled licence in amusements not worth the trouble of breaking line for, much less rioting over, endured for six months – all through one cold weather – and then we thought that the heat and the knowledge of having lost his money and health and lamed his horses would sober The Boy down, and he would stand steady. In ninety-nine cases out of a hundred this would have happened. You can see the principle working in any Indian Station. But this particular case fell through because The Boy was sensitive and took things seriously – as I may have said some seven times before. Of course, we could not tell how his excesses struck him personally. They were nothing very heartbreaking or above the average. . . . But he must have taken another view altogether, and have believed himself ruined beyond redemption. His Colonel talked to him severely when the cold weather ended. That made him more wretched than ever; and it was only an ordinary 'Colonel's wigging'! . . .

The thing that kicked the beam in The Boy's mind was a remark that a woman made when he was talking to her. There is no use in repeating it, for it was only a cruel little sentence, rapped out before thinking, that made him flush to the roots of his hair. He kept himself to himself for three days, and then put in for two days' leave to go shooting near a Canal Engineer's Rest House about thirty miles out. He got his leave, and that night at Mess was noisier and more offensive than ever. He said that he was 'going to shoot big game', and left at half-past ten o'clock in an *ekka*. Partridge – which was the only thing a man could get near the Rest House – is not big game; so every one laughed. . . .

Rudyard Kipling, Plain Tales from the Hills

Contents

Contents

Illustrations

Preface

This study on madness and colonialism has experienced a great many changes of direction and emphasis during the last seven years. It started off as a project on 'Mad Colonialists' (in the Sociology Department at the University of Konstanz), became a doctoral thesis on 'Psychiatry and Colonialism' (in the Department of the History of South Asia at the University of London), and finally emerged in its present form as 'Mad Tales from the Raj' during an extended period of research into the social history of medicine (at the Wellcome Institute for the History of Medicine, London) and some months of productive withdrawal to the exciting remoteness of the antipodes (Department of History at Victoria University of Wellington). The final outcome is, not surprisingly, an interdisciplinary approach. My original training as a cultural psychologist and political scientist, involvement in the sociology of developing countries and intercultural communication, and subsequent study of the history of South Asia and of the history of medicine, helped to cut across various different disciplines. This may be considered as an advantage by some. Others may assess the outcome as an eclectic or even shallow attempt to break into the well-guarded territory of several branches of the social sciences. There may also be those who will take offence at a critical account of British colonialism, and yet others who will believe psychiatry and medicine to be beyond the scrutiny of scientific and political investigation.

I have had the opportunity of speaking on the subject during the different stages of its 'metamorphosis': at the Sociology Department at Konstanz University, the Departmental Seminar in Sociology and Social Anthropology at Keele University, the

Preface

European Conference on Modern South Asian Studies in Taellberg, Sweden, the Post-Graduate Seminar in History at the School of Oriental and African Studies, London, the Wellcome Unit at University College London, the Workshop of the European Ayurvedic Society in London, the Conference of the Medical Sociology Group of the British Sociological Association in York, the Society for the Social History of Medicine's Conference at the University of Aston, and the Departmental Seminar in History, Victoria University of Wellington. I learnt much from the discussion ensuing on each of these occasions.

I am indebted to Professor Detlef Kantowsky who cradled the original idea of evaluating the *Records of Pembroke House and Ealing Lunatic Asylum, 1818–1892* (available in the India Office Records, London). I also want to express thanks to Professor Kenneth Ballhatchet who read through several long-winded versions of my thesis and provided invaluable advice and information. I am further indebted to Professor David Arnold and Dr Roy Porter for their critical interest, emotional encouragement, and their helpful remarks on contents and style. Thanks also to Dr W.F. Bynum, Uli Weigel, MA, and Dr T. Beaglehole who commented on various parts of the manuscript. Special thanks are due to Dr Michael Williams for struggling through a verbose, teutonic syntax with a temperate Anglo-Saxon mind and a constructive editorial pencil; and for providing emotional support during various bleak and difficult stages.

I am grateful for the financial resources that enabled me to pursue this study. Thanks are due to the Fördererverein der Universität Konstanz, the British Council, the German Historical Institute, London, the Wellcome Trust, and the University of Wellington. I greatly appreciate the authentic interest shown in my topic by Gill Davies of Routledge, who made the publication of my material possible. And last but not least I wish to express my thanks for the help of librarians and archivists at the British Library, the Library of the School of Oriental and African Studies, the Library of the Senate House, University of London, the Library of the Wellcome Institute for the History of Medicine, and, above all, the India Office Library and Records.

Wellington
August 1990

xi

Introduction: *Ex oriente lux* – the light of the Orient

Some 'mysterious transformation' is said to have affected Westerners once they proceeded East of Suez.[1] The view that experience of life in an alien Eastern country set travellers and expatriates apart from their fellow countrymen was common amongst those who reflected upon the effect on generations of Europeans of *ex oriente lux*, the 'light of the Orient'. So much was the East–West encounter perceived as leaving its mark on people's personality that those who had lived in the Orient for some time were regarded as a 'distinct species'. Their peculiar views, attitudes, and behaviour were both excused and explained by reference to life abroad, and on return to Europe they were treated 'either with awed bewilderment or humorous ridicule'. What sparked off this 'mysterious transformation' has, since the eighteenth century, been subject to speculation. Some assumed that it was the alien environment that was to blame, in that polite manners and sociable behaviour were 'jungled out' of those exposed to prolonged life in the tropical forests and arid plains of the Indian peninsula.[2] Others were inclined to see the lack of 'restraint of parents, relatives and friends' as upsetting the mental balance and emotional inhibition of a number of those young, predominantly male, *griffins*, or green newcomers, who, being 'thrown together' with others of their age, became 'violent and intractable'.[3] Yet others in contrast have been disposed to deepen the mystery still further by denying that anybody who had no first-hand experience of life in the East could 'ever really understand what it was like'[4] – thus pre-empting any attempt by the uninitiated to come to grips with the factors which are said to have made all expatriates 'members of one great family, aliens under one sky'.[5]

1

Figure 1 Lunatic Asylum, Madras, 1852 (plan elevations and sections). (Reproduced by permission of the India Office Library and Records and the British Library, London.)

Plan Elevations and Sections of the **LUNATIC HOSPITAL** *at Madras.*

Back Elevation — Section thro A.B. — Section thro CD — Front Elevation — Scale to Sections — Scale to Plan

... contrast the basis of Surgeon Conolly's reputation with that of Surgeon Cantor. Conolly certainly belonged to the 'old breed' of Company servants, who came to India in search of fortune, found it, and returned home to Britain to enjoy their retirement in ease and luxury. They did usually not excel in anything of a strictly professional kind, although they might be remembered for those activities that gained them their wealth. (As, in Conolly's case, the ... military officers ... in contrast practised ... himself rather than merely as a conduit to trade and financial speculation. He was regarded by his colleagues on the medical board as a competent practitioner and had got as close to recognition as an expert in the treatment of the mad as any medical officer in India in the period. He had been superintendent of the lunatic asylum at ..., had published a report on his work there, and ... in India, entrusted with re-organizing the ... managed Calcutta lunatic asylum. He also superintended and reformed the native lunatic asylum in Bhadrak... Cantor was not unaware of his prominent position as the province's first officially acknowledged expert in lunacy. He proudly cited his experience in South East Asia, and frequently referred knowledgeably to asylum management as practised in England and ... though never failing to point out that circum... ... different owed much to the fact that the former had established his fame at a period when becoming a 'native' was still seen as a normal and legitimate aspiration. Cantor, in contrast, took up ... that ... not only the standards of his own ... but also those of the East India Company demanded that medical officer should be reasonably well qualified, and should devote their time and energy primarily to their medical ...

Whilst a variety of explanations have been advanced for the precise nature of the European's alleged character change under conditions of 'heat and dust' in the Orient's plains and hills, one specific dimension of the East–West mystery has commonly been agreed upon: travellers, merchants, diplomats, and soldiers from a variety of different lands were susceptible to it. The psychological metamorphosis of the English has, nevertheless, been characterized as quite distinct from the process of cultural adaptation incurred by members of other European nations. It was the 'insularity of the English character' (said to have been as marked in the eighteenth as in the nineteenth century), which made the English 'persist on their customs and habits of life even in most unfavourable circumstances'.[6] The melancholic traits to which the 'inhabitants of England were doomed by geographic accident'[7] were said to have made it difficult for them to endure solitude[8] or 'the ordinary misfortunes of existence'[9] – let alone unfamiliar circumstances 'in a clime so remote from their own'.[10] The upshot was the exacerbation of those character traits which in the British Isles were at worst looked upon as signs of eccentricity or a sensitive or nervous disposition. In India they turned into 'an exaggerated and vulgarised edition', 'modified by climatic conditions', and more visibly and literally out-of-place because of the lack of 'the tradition and continuity of English society'.[11]

Despite variation in emphasis, these images of what made the English in the Orient a 'species apart' were reproduced time and again during the last three centuries. Such popular speculations, taken up and dwelled on by many a scholar, may contain a grain of truth. Exposure to unfamiliar cultural conditions does in fact have psychological consequences characterized by a variety of emotional and behavioural coping strategies, of which anxiety, anger, or depression are the most common, usually followed by a tendency to either overadapt or respond with aggressive hostility to the alien environment.[12] It is certainly the case that British government officials and military officers in India, for example, remained in most circumstances aloof from their Indian subjects, and the observation that, unlike the English, the French and the Portuguese have – for better or worse – cultivated a less detached and less socially inhibited stance towards Eastern people may indicate existing differences in the way in which members of different nations react to unfamiliar situations.

However, the flaw in the hackneyed images of the nature of British colonial rule in India is that they are redolent of an anglocentric ideology. Most British accounts of the 'mysterious transformation' of character during the British Raj are in fact limited to the *English* – thus ignoring the presence of the Scottish, Irish, and Welsh who (whilst they would presumably reject outright any suggestion of affinity with the English in either temperament or manners) have nevertheless been an important factor in British–Indian policy and social life. The possibility of highly diverse impacts of the 'alien' on Britons of different social backgrounds, and of diverse behavioural responses to life in the East, is tacitly avoided – although the distinctive importance of social precedence and the marked differences in Europeans' lifestyles have been widely reported, and since the eighteenth century have become part and parcel of most accounts of British social life in the East. These omissions are not merely the result of an imprecise use of language. They indicate a tendency in the fictional, biographic, and historical literature to present the British–Indian encounter in an almost exclusively English light and from the point of view of those 'who ruled India'.

Apart from a few authors such as the ubiquitous Kipling, most widely-read accounts of the British in India have conveyed the myth that colonial society was differentiated simply into an English ruling elite on the one side,[13] and an amorphous (though reputedly gorgeously colourful) mass of 'native' subjects, higgledy-piggledy subsumed under the label of 'Mohamedans' on the other.[14] Such oversimplification has served a still lingering imperial ideology, wallowing in the idea of a homogeneous ruling class, united by a noble vision, and with supreme self-confidence devoted to the colonizing duty. An ethnically and socially discrete ruling class in India emerged, so the story has it, towards the end of the eighteenth century, when the time came for

> the flowering, the highest peak perhaps in the lofty range of what the English have done, when a handful of our countrymen, by the integrity of their character and with not much else to help them, gave to many millions for the first time for some centuries the idea that a ruler might be concerned with their well-being.[15]

One factor which slowed down the progress of moralization was the emergence of a new paradigm of dealing with the mentally ill... the doctrine of... based on the assumption that the insane were essentially human, though lacking in self-control and discipline. By substituting physical restraint and punishment by kindness and moral education, the Tukes, the main proponents of "moral" therapy in Britain, had achieved great... Most specifically, however, the Tukes had also argued...

Tank

Figure 2 Lunatic Asylum, Madras, 1852 (ground plan). (Reproduced by permission of the India Office Library and Records and the British Library, London.)

Oversimplification is however not the monopoly of imperial ideology alone. A number of anti-imperialist accounts have in their turn been based on the similarly sweeping assumption that colonial society could simply be dichotomized into the white colonialist elite on the one hand and exploited 'natives' on the other.

Yet the European community in areas administered by the East India Company by the end of the eighteenth century not only consisted in fact of people with an English, Scottish, Irish, or Welsh regional background, interspersed with people of mixed race, and nationals of European countries who had been taken on in recruiting depots on the Continent, but also of a large number belonging to what could be called the poor, or lower classes. To people of such a variety of cultural and social backgrounds life in India not only had different meanings, but also affected them in a variety of different ways. For a start the decision to sign on for a passage to India in the service of the East India Company would in the case of lower-class soldiers most typically have been induced by harsh economic necessity, and the guarded hope that – with a bit of luck – some of the recruiting sergeants' promises of the lure of service in the East might come true. Members of the higher or middle classes, in contrast, while not devoid of material motives, would at least potentially have been in a position more socially advantageous to devotion not only to reflection on the East's serendipitous material bounties but also on its spiritual and cultural offerings and mysteries. Lacking any interest in the latter, they could be free – to the extent of snobbish ennui – to engage in those social activities which had been characteristic of decadent upper-class life at home.

A young man of 20, with the optimistic name of John Luck, for example, left his native Lincolnshire during the trade recession of 1838 for military duty in the East India Company's artillery, as he was 'not happy trayiling in the contry for work', and admitted after three years of service in Bengal 'i ham so ancious to se my dear native home agane . . . as i know too well this country would soon kill me', imploring his mother 'if for ever o a due, sell not my ole close'.[16] He would certainly have experienced the East quite differently from, say, Lord Auckland, governor-general from 1835 to 1842, who was according to his sister mainly 'bored' by the splendid extravaganzas and ceremonial spectacles put on for his amusement while touring North India.[17]

Such a comparison of the experiences of selected lower-class persons with those of particular gentlemen of respectable means and status, however, is not meant to imply that social class was the only factor affecting people's various responses to life in a foreign land. It certainly is important to point out that the popular image of life in the East tends to concentrate on the whims and woes of higher-class people, and is at best to be seen as highly selective, and at worst as functioning to mystify imperial rule as gentlemanly power. Yet colonial myths ought to be refuted by reference to historical accounts that reflect the variety and social complexity of daily life in response to both the politics of colonial rule and the alien Indian environment and culture. Whilst being to the manner born will have made a satisfying experience and successful career in the East more probable, it certainly did not guarantee it. There are examples of ordinary soldiers who, contrary to popular opinion, appreciated Indian ways of life and preferred residence in India to the more familiar life in the British Isles. And some members of the higher classes expressed their fascination with and attraction to Eastern ways of thinking and living, or alternatively failed utterly to gain fame and fortune.

Take the example of Richard Compton, on military duty in South India from 1856 to 1858. He often felt 'quite desperate and ill', confessing that he was 'so very very lonely', and 'heartily sick of the Army', and in fact was sure that he would 'never do any good in it'.[18] Yet he emphasized that he liked India 'amazingly' and thought it a 'glorious country'. Similarly, seven soldiers petitioned the Madras Government to be allowed to stay on after having spent between twelve and twenty-six years in the service of the King's or the Company's troops. They argued that not only would they feel like aliens and without economic future back in England, but that also they wished to stay with their Indian wives and the children borne by them.[19] And last but not least, Captain Thomas Williamson, author of the famous *East-India Vade-Mecum; or, Complete Guide to Gentlemen intended for the Civil, Military, or Naval Service of the Honorable East India Company*, expressed in 1810 his opinion that Indians were a 'race whose intellectual qualities, whatever may be said by ignorant or designing men, are at least on a par with those of Europeans'.[20]

Life in India stood for many things for people who planned to spend some time in the East. For some it was the land of mysteries or of regrets, of unfulfilled hopes, the El Dorado of their dreams, the land of milk and honey, where a prosperous career could easily be made, or else an escape found from economic hardship or professional failure at home, a self-imposed punishment for past personal wrongdoings, a challenge or a place where passions and predilections could be uninhibitedly expressed. In the face of such great variety of individual dreams, expectations, hopes, longings, and projections it seems vital to resist any temptation to judge all expatriates' perceptions and experiences of India alike, or in consideration of their class background alone.

Any account of the way in which mentally ill members of the European community in British India were treated during the days of the East India Company will consequently have to go beyond the idealized and one-sided popular image of the British Raj. Similarly, it will have to open up the narrow and myopic 'medical gaze', and attempt to lend a voice to what Foucault called mental institutions' 'silent inmate inventories', by squarely locating medical and psychological treatment and patients' life stories within their wider, socio-cultural and economic context.[21]

What then were the features characteristic of British social life in India? The social context within which, say, the young writer, or clerk, from Europe would have found himself on arrival in one of the ports of entry in India towards the middle of the eighteenth century was that of a small, closely-knit and hierarchically-organized expatriate community, living in quarters separate from Indian society. In Bengal the European community in the 1750s amounted to only seventy-six civil servants of the Company, 500 officers and soldiers, and about 100 non-official Europeans.[22] At the top-end of this enclave of Europeans would be the president or governor who was, according to one historian

> a being poised midway . . . between heaven and earth, to
> the settlement a sort of tutelary deity, to Indian ambassadors and durbars the representative of the Britannic

Majesty, and to the Directors [of the Company] an
inveterate object of suspicion. . . . he kept up considerable
state; he never went abroad . . . without being attended by
eighty armed peons as well as English guards, with two
Union flags carried before him and 'country musick
enough to frighten a stranger into belief the men were
mad'.[23]

Closely behind the governor, with less regal splendour but still
high social status, followed the members of his council and
other senior Company officials, military officers, merchants and
planters. The next social layer of the European settlement
consisted of soldiers, sailors, and minor Company servants who
lived a life apart from the civilian and military elite and spent
their time off-duty, so it is reported, amongst their own kind,
frequenting the hospital and the nearby punch-houses. The
professions would be sparsely represented, with but a few
chaplains, surgeons, barristers and teachers.[24] Similarly,
European women would be scarce. This lack was compensated
for by the then widespread and socially accepted practice of
'domiciling' Indian women.[25] Although the British kept aloof
from Indian society even during the reputedly open-minded
century of the Enlightenment, they were willing to adopt the
excrescences of those Indian customs which made life more
comfortable and luxurious.[26] The maintenance of Indian mis-
tresses was one such example of the Europeans' Indianization.
It was generally approved of until early in the nineteenth century and had obvious financial advantages.

European wives were costly to keep, so that it was much easier
to support 'a whole zenana of Indians than the extravagance of
one English lady'.[27] The small sum of between £2 and £4 per
month attendant upon concubinage was considered to have
been more compatible with the financial means of an average
civil servant or officer.[28] A British wife, in contrast, would
require dressmakers, hairdressers, ladies' maids, and other
major expenses, which could add up to about £300 per year – a
tidy sum which, it was held, pressed hard on a husband in
respectable circumstances who would in addition have to spend
about £600 per annum to entertain a middle-class establishment
in Calcutta, without even the luxury of a garden-house in the
cooler suburbs, exclusive of a carriage and frequent parties to
entertain his friends. Given the small official salaries of £27 for

a writer and £132 for a council member, most civil and military servants would not have been able to keep a European woman in any style.

Financial considerations alone could, however, not have accounted for the attraction of Indian wives. Even the cost of an average household which allowed a young bachelor to live if not in luxury at least in reasonable style, would exceed by far his regular income. But then, hardly any Company servant relied on the small salary afforded to him by the Company's directors. After all, the second part of the eighteenth century was the period when really big fortunes could be made in the East, and the luckier and more cunning Company official, military officer or free merchant, trader and planter would return to Britain as a 'nabob'. The 1750s and 1760s in particular were considered the heyday of 'unbridled corruption and bribery'.[29] Although not all members of the European community shared in the acquisition of the East's bounty (and could therefore afford or be inclined to engage in excess and merrymaking), an ostentatious lifestyle which would have made the reputedly dazzling entertainments of Vauxhall and the Brighton Pavilion appear as mere side-shows, was characteristic of the *nouveaux-riches* in the East.

Although it seems that conspicuous parading of one's riches owed much to Oriental rulers' extravagance and splendour, this lifestyle was not dissimilar to that of the upper classes in late eighteenth-century England. William Hickey, a man of 'amorous disposition' and familiar with the 'nocturnal dissoluteness' in London and Calcutta, travelled India during the reign of King George III and depicted in knowledgeable detail orgiastic banquets (and subsequent hangovers).[30] In his *Memoirs* he pointed up the striking similarity between the entertainments of polite and moneyed society in London and Calcutta, describing both as 'frivolous, unscrupulous, immersed in fashion, addicted to heavy eating, hard drinking, gambling, and duelling'. A crucial difference between the grandee in London and the 'nabob' in India was, however, that the latter was typically middle class in origin, and upper class only in manners. This fact may have contributed to some of the sneering on the part of refined English society at the 'nabob' who returned to England and bought himself into parliament and upper-class social circles. At the same time the European community in India itself lacked a strong middle class, generating instead a

12

'middle-class aristocracy',[31] which not only assumed an aristocratic style of living but could rule over the Indian population without making any concessions to the demands of any middle-class expatriate community.

During the decades leading up to the Indian revolt or Mutiny of 1857 things changed drastically. For one thing, the Company's involvement in the East gradually shifted from commerce to the expansion and administration of territory. Along with this change (which has been poignantly characterized as a shift from 'mere collection of *loot* . . . to orderly, if still burdensome, administration') went an increase in the number of Europeans and a growing sense of community spirit which set the British ever more apart from Indian social circles.[32] In consequence of Pitt's Act of 1784, which established a joint government of Company and Crown, and the crucial administrative reforms undertaken during the 1780s and 1790s by Cornwallis, service for the Company became more of an adequately paid career and less of an adventure and opportunity to accumulate a fortune by corruption, patronage and connections. Lord Cornwallis, who 'came as a reformer of abuses with plenary powers, and brought with him the viewpoint of the India House and Whitehall, no previous knowledge of the country, and a lack of that imaginative sympathy which would have made up for his ignorance' achieved not only a gradual purge of corruption but a widening of the racial and social gulf.[33] His phrase 'every native of Hindustan, I verily believe, is corrupt', became an oft-quoted guiding principle of the British approach to racial relations during the nineteenth century, and succinctly expressed the growing belief that Indian society was intrinsically inferior and had to be subordinated to European guidance – a view which culminated in the Victorians' ideology of their civilizing mission.

Sharpened racial discrimination also implied that the maintenance of the ruler's prestige became a central theme of government policy, and of the way affairs of daily life were conducted. Indians were, for example, excluded from higher government offices, and on the more petty, though psychologically and symbolically important, level of social etiquette, chairs were no longer provided for spectators in legal courts, and, in Calcutta, Company clerks 'expected every Indian to salute them'.[34] The social hierarchy amongst the European community was no less affected by the ruling class's concern to preserve the image of the British character. The behaviour of the steadily increasing number of lower-class Europeans (soldiers, sailors, and minor clerks, and in particular down-and-outs such as deserters, vagabonds, prostitutes, and drunkards) consequently became a concern which was to be complemented and sustained during the nineteenth century by the ideology of the Poor Law: 'not so much . . . to help the unfortunate as to stigmatize the self-confessed failures of society'.[35] When, for example, soldiers left military stations and started roaming the country they drew the uneasy attention of civil authorities and political agents. Although it was asserted that 'pecuniary aid is easily given in these cases', the main problem was rather that of 'lowering the European Character in the eyes of the Natives'.[36] Consequently the measure most frequently resorted to was that of ultimate deportation back to England, following punishment and incarceration in India.

The Company's organizational development from the middle of the eighteenth century to the Indian revolt of 1857 was both reflected in and sustained by a corresponding shift in social and racial relations, and in a reorganization of the European community itself. It had been the male adventurers and merchants who came to India for commerce during the age of Enlightenment; it was the soldiers and administrators who accompanied them to annex and govern from the end of the eighteenth century onwards; and finally it was European women who increasingly rounded off the hitherto more or less exclusively male European community during the nineteenth century. And in most cases they brought with them their 'insular whims and prejudices, which no official contact with Indians or iron compulsion of loneliness ever tempted them to abandon'.[37] As a consequence the expatriate community not only grew into an increasingly socially stratified society but also had developed, by the middle of the nineteenth century, all the symptoms of full-blown racial discrimination and social prejudice.

This attitude of 'airy disdain and flippant contempt' had, as the historian Spear asserted, a 'background of fear which an unknown and incalculable environment is liable to excite in everyone' – a fear which may partly account for the ferocity with which racial and social relations were imbued. Indians were referred to in a derogatory way as 'blacks', 'natives', and 'brutes', if not in the court room, at least in the drawing room.[38]

14

Whilst all Europeans were equally subjected to English constitutional principles, special legal provision was made to restrict the influx to India of poor Europeans, and to punish and deport undesirable down-and-outs who were considered to 'vex, harass and perplex the weak natives' and to thereby harm the high prestige in which the British liked to think they were held by Indians.[39]

A special social development, occasioned by the colonial nature of the British presence in India, was the emergence of a strong military barrack culture, sharply separated from the small European stations' civil lines and the towns. Shortly after the Indian revolt, in 1861, the European civilian population in the whole of India amounted to about one fourth of the military community (namely to 22,556 and 84,083, respectively, exclusive of 19,306 women).[40] A further important factor in the making of racial and social relations was the steadily growing number of people of mixed race. Although British–Indian liaisons had in the eighteenth century implicitly been approved of, the offspring of such relations had to a certain extent always been considered a socially undesirable consequence – unless the children's father was of high rank and would provide for the more fair-skinned of his descendants to be educated in England.[41] With but rare exception, by the beginning of the nineteenth century people of mixed race, or Eurasians, lived on the margins of both Indian and European society, although they made up a numerically significant part of the cities' populations. In 1822 the Christian population of Calcutta, for example, was calculated to have been 13,138, of which only 2,254 were Europeans, while the rest, namely 10,884, were of Eurasian extraction.[42]

The changes which occurred between 1750 and 1858 in the Company's administration and European social life were considerable. Although greatly furthered by contingent circumstances and stimulated and modified by local peculiarities, these developments were no less significant than (nor were they independent of) the changes that occurred in Britain during the same period. Any sensible investigation of the 'transformation of the British character' in the East would consequently have to take cognizance of its historical dimension, and would further have to see it as much a product of developments in the imperial motherland as of Indian specificities. In an attempt to characterize the changes in the

British policy towards India the historian Stokes pointed out
that

> the loose, tolerant attitude of [Company officials such as]
> Clive and Hastings, their readiness to admire and work
> through Indian institutions, their practical grasp of the
> British position, unclouded by sentiments of racial
> superiority or a sense of mission, were ultimately the
> reflection of eighteenth-century England. The trans-
> formation of the Englishman from nabob to sahib was also
> fundamentally an English and not an Indian trans-
> formation, however much events assisted the process.
> Indian experience undoubtedly hardened certain traits in
> the English character, but for their origin one needs to
> penetrate to the genesis of the nineteenth-century English
> middle class, and to the hidden springs setting its type.[43]

In fact, the popular contemporary self-perception, too,
changed from that of British involvement in the East as a
commercial enterprise and lucrative adventure under taxing
environmental conditions, to that of the 'white man's burden'
amongst alien peoples. It thus expressed and grasped one
aspect of changing socio-economic and historical conditions.
What both the Georgian merchant-adventurers and the
Victorian civil and military servants shared and bore, either with
the equanimity or fervid over-statement typical of their res-
pective period, was the burden of their own social culture which
they could not but carry along with them.

1

Madness and the politics of colonial rule

Ideological positions

Writings on the Raj have typically been fuelled by political interests and nearly always served some particular ideological purpose. James Mill's *History of British India* (1817), for example, represents an early attempt by a distinguished protagonist of utilitarianism and advocate of post-Enlightenment values, to provide support for the idea of converting the Indian sub-continent into a nation governed by reason, fed by European knowledge. There were many other accounts, both preceding and following Mill's description of pre-European India as a society characterized by despotic rule and barbarism, and of Europeans' corruption and idle high living, or devotion to duty. Some of these wallowed in a vision of the spirit of enlightenment, or, more militantly, the *pax britannica* dispersing over the Indian peninsula, and advanced gruesome details of violent Indian customs (such as the burning of widows, mutilation of children and strangling of travellers) as evidence for the necessity of westernization. Others (of which there were fewer) attempted to adduce evidence as to why India was no longer 'worth keeping'.

Diversity is however not confined to the realm of fiction and scientific writing. It is in fact liable to characterize any but the most totalitarian political system. Government officials in India, too, espoused a variety of different ideological positions, personal interests, and idiosyncracies. Discussion of any aspect of government is therefore bound to reflect this. Lunacy policy is no exception. Take the example of the Bombay council during Lord Falkland's governorship in the late 1840s and early

Figure 3 European Lunatic Asylum, Calcutta, early nineteenth
century. (Reproduced by permission of the India Office Library and
Records and the British Library, London.)

1850s. Although unsavoury allusions to officials' private life were then made less frequently than only a few decades earlier, when Bombay society sweltered in a 'continual effervescence of scandal and gossip', tempers were still inflamed by widely different opinions on the province's administration, especially in acerbic discussions of the allocation of public resources.[1] A long dispute ensued, for example, when improved institutional facilities were discussed for the province's chronically insane.

'The subject of lunacy', asserted Falkland finally with fervour in 1850, 'is engaging and will continue to engage my attention'.[2] The governor, renowned for his humanitarian attitude and benevolent spirit, and very much liked by both the European and Parsi communities, strongly supported a proposal by the medical authorities to provide 'amply' and 'on the most approved system' for the treatment of the province's lunatics. The other council members in contrast, mostly old India-hands of many years standing (unlike Falkland, who had recently arrived from England) found such expense 'quite out of the question'. They held that more important areas needed government's attention, and that 'in this and in many similar cases we have not merely to consider what is *desirable*, but what can be afforded'.[3] Consequently the plans for a new asylum in the province were put on ice despite numerous reports of the old premises' overcrowded conditions.

Disagreements between council members, governor, commander-in-chief, and governor-general were reflected in many dissenting minutes sent to England with the request for outside arbitration by the Company's London authorities. The Bombay government in particular appears to have had a long history of disagreement amongst its civil and military servants who were renowned for their 'intractable temper',[4] and for only slowly developing from parochialists with 'minds of the average country town' to a more cosmopolitan and open-minded species of colonialists.[5] In some instances personality clashes and the tense atmosphere of a small closely-knit community of expatriates played a crucial role. Tempers were also aroused by ethnic tensions, with Irish, Scottish, Welsh, and English officials accusing each other of jobbery and nepotism.

Henry Dundas, a Scotsman, for example, was influential on account of his position as president of the board of control, a parliamentary body set up in London in 1784 to supervise and direct the Company's civil and military policy in India, and, under Dundas's firm leadership, the ultimate arbiter of political decisions. He was accused of (and envied for) securing positions in the Company's employ for his favourites – a tendency which some ideologues of British colonialism nevertheless thought 'put India in his debt'.[6] A certain tension between military and civil servants, too, appears to have been a characteristic prolegomenon to policy making. Lord Dalhousie, governor-general from 1848 to 1856, for example, strongly disapproved of Sir Charles Napier's, (the commander-in-chief), actions in the Punjab, and finally accomplished not only his adversary's resignation, but the establishment of the unequivocal superiority of the governor-general's position over that of the commander-in-chief.

It was not always financial prudence alone which led to antagonism and controversy. Nor was it simply personal grudges and nationalistic or professional chauvinism that could kindle administrators' passion. Some officials were seriously disposed towards the idea of impressing their ideological position on India. This vast area of land, allegedly peopled with inferior races and subjected to despotic tyranny would, (from the point of view of the Benthamite or liberal reformer as much as from the spiritual heights of an evangelical zealot) greatly benefit from the imposition of what some considered to be the most advanced and progressive socio-political regimes. Many ideologues consequently used their prominent position in the Company's administration to pursue their favourite political brainchild.

John Stuart Mill and even more so his father James, for example, both important members of the Company's executive government in England, were in a position to leave a decided utilitarian mark on some relevant matters of policy making. James Mill himself was very much aware of this privileged situation, describing in a somewhat inflated fashion his job as being the 'internal government of 60 millions of people'.[7] In a similar vein his son, John Stuart Mill, proclaimed that his father had to a great extent been able to 'throw into his draft of despatches, and to carry through the ordeal of the Court of Directors and Board of Control, without having their force much weakened, his real opinions on Indian subjects'.[8] A Benthamite influence seeped through to India – and not only via despatches from England.

At the Indian end of government, too, utilitarianism had its advocates. Lord Bentinck, for example, had, on occasion of a farewell dinner with a small though distinguished circle of utilitarians on the eve of his call to India as governor-general, been feasted on 'the pure milk of the Benthamite word', and was, on his arrival in Calcutta, advised by one of Bentham's disciples. Bentham consequently wrote to Bentinck full of joy that he felt as if 'the golden age of British India were lying before me'.[9] Similarly, Mountstuart Elphinstone, governor of Bombay from 1819 to 1827 (and close friend of Edward Strachey, a 'Utilitarian and Democrat by creed' and along with James Mill employed as assistant examiner in the India Office in London) put a distinct Benthamite mark on the administration of civil affairs in his province.[10] He was also a great advocate of Bentham's 'panopticon' idea and had been responsible for experiments with large-scale public institutions in Bombay nearly two decades before similar plans were considered for the supreme province of Bengal.

Utilitarianism did however not only stand for the support of large institutions, although this was certainly a most important aspect during an era pregnant with what Foucault came to describe as the 'great confinement'. Utilitarians favoured a centralized system of asylum provision in place of patchy measures such as had been implemented on a more or less *ad hoc* and uncoordinated basis and (as Bentham would have seen it) in a dilettante and not always rational way at the local level of colonial administration. Bentham himself did much to spur the lunacy reform movement in England, advocating not only the establishment of large-scale and specialized institutions, managed by experts and subject to regular control and inspection, but also a consolidated national lunacy policy based upon rational principles rather than mere discretionary decisions by non-experts. The system of lunacy provision that was to emerge in British India by the middle of the century owed a great deal to the utilitarians' 'science of government'.

The surprisingly short discussion in 1820 of the erection of the Bombay Lunatic Asylum bears evidence of this.[11] The decision to have an institution built that could lodge as many as one hundred patients implied asylum construction on a, for the times, unprecedented scale. Sanction of such an ambitious project by both the Bombay council and the London authorities was remarkable. It was certainly not due to indifference or lack of reflection in a period when the provincial governments in

India were expected by the Company to curtail public expenditure.

The Bombay medical officers who had initiated the proposal argued in terms of long-term cost-effectiveness and service-efficiency, and (obviously to the full satisfaction of both Elphinstone and his council, and the London officials) suggested that a less extensive and expensive system than that in Bengal should be established in Bombay. In Bengal several lunatic asylums for Indians continued to exist in different parts of the province despite the Company Court's orders and in addition to a separate, private institution for Europeans in the capital.[12] Admittedly, other factors than merely a Benthamite disposition were at work here, such as a less forceful inclination in Bombay to separate Indians from Europeans, and reluctance by Bombay officials to simply mimic the supreme province's lunacy policies as had recently been decreed by the Court in London. A certain panopticon-enthusiasm is however easily discernible, despite the fact that the asylum on its completion in 1826 and, incidentally, on the eve of governor Elphinstone's departure from India, provided for only half the number of inmates for which it had originally been planned.[13]

The idea of 'panopticon' and the complementary principles of economies of scale, and centralized and rationalized provision for the mentally ill, was not put to rest though. In 1849/50 the question of whether lunacy provision ought to be decentralized and several small institutions built in the various provinces or whether one single receptacle near Bombay would be more cost-efficient and cure-effective was once again laid before the Bombay council.[14] This administrative and political question had become more pressing since the annexation of Sind and the Punjab, with new and vast areas of land, and peoples with a culture of their own, to be governed from Bombay. The Bombay medical board was still attuned to the 'panopticon' idea and therefore strongly in favour of large institutions, maintaining that 'more benefit at a moderate cost would be produced on a certain number of Insanes by their being accommodated and treated in large, rather than in small asylums'.[15]

In the event, and not uncharacteristically, the council failed to arrive at a joint decision and shifted the matter on to London in 1853. The authorities there were strongly in favour of keeping the system – albeit on a more restricted scale – as it had developed until then, maintaining that financial prudence as much as common sense told against a single new large institution. How could a place possibly be found that would be 'central' enough in an area where transfer from remote districts to Bombay was almost as nonsensical as shifting lunatics all the way from London to St Petersburg?[16] The idea of large-scale or 'mammoth' asylums and of their centralized administration had been bred for western Europe's industrialized centres and its more easily accessible and comparatively small hinterlands. In India, however, distances posed a challenging logistic problem. Too few lunatics of both European and Indian descent seen as fit subjects for institutionalization, were dispersed over too large an area. Thus, unlike in Britain's industrialized urban conglomerates and rural centres, 'panopticon' and with it a system of centralized asylum provision was not yet a practicable solution for colonial India. Consequently, several medium-sized establishments in the main centres of population were kept open, the smallest and most dilapidated ones were discontinued, and the idea of a 'panopticon' was dropped – for the time being.

Utilitarians were not the only political visionaries who strived to realize their aspirations in India. An evangelical strain of thought was being nurtured by Charles Grant, a member of the 'Clapham Sect' who used his influence as director and chairman of the East India Company to ensure that India would be opened up for their civilizing mission. His pressure group succeeded in having India thrown open to the religious zeal of missionaries from 1813 onwards. He was also partially successful in – though not solely responsible for – the restrictions on the number of lower-class Europeans who were permitted to emigrate to or stay on in India. 'Low and licentious' Europeans, if let loose on the 'weak natives', would 'vex, harass and perplex' them, Grant argued, and would be detrimental to the ultimate noble aim of colonial rule of spreading 'our light and knowledge'.[17] Grant's argument appealed in its essence beyond militant evangelicals to many members of the respectable British community in India. They were keen to prevent destitute sailors, vagrants, deserters, lunatics, and such like from becoming a 'threat and nuisance' on every street corner of the trim and neat European parts of their towns.[18] The policy of sending European lunatics back to England, which was made official for all provinces under British rule from 1818 onwards, owed much to his street- and mind-cleaning mentality (notwithstanding the logistical problems it posed).[19]

Less proselytizingly than Grant, but not thereby less effectively, a whiggish mark was left by administrators such as Lord Auckland, who controlled Indian affairs in his capacity as governor-general from 1836 to 1842. In regard to lunacy policy he insisted on as little intervention by the state as possible. He consequently thwarted attempts by the Bengal medical board to get rid of the privately owned and managed European Lunatic Asylum and its stubborn proprietor who continually demanded greater latitude than the province's medical officers were willing to grant. Although the place served only as a temporary receptacle for patients awaiting a passage back to England, it constituted not only an essential part of the city's medical institutions but also a lucrative income source for its owner. At the time private ownership of asylums and instruments to ensure public control of their internal affairs was being heatedly debated in England. Auckland's 'hands-off' policy was therefore somewhat out of step with recent trends in the metropolitan public health sector, where the powers of controlling bodies such as the commissioners in lunacy were in the process of being extended in an attempt to guarantee close surveillance of public institutions as well as of private entrepreneurs in the medical sector.

It took another decade, until 1856, and the more autocratic style of government of Lord Dalhousie, to impart to lunacy policy in Bengal, too, 'those great measures of internal improvement' which he was so 'desirous of promoting' during his term of office in British India.[20] In practice, Dalhousie put an end to the previous *laissez-faire* approach in the Bengal 'mad-business'. He established a 'Government Lunatic Asylum' in Calcutta which was to be supervised by an experienced medical officer, regulated by a strict set of rules, and controlled not by a board of medicos (whose rambling discussions Dalhousie loathed and deemed unproductive) but by the province's single director-general.[21]

Bureaucracy, corruption, and public opinion

Different ideologies and styles of leadership resulted in a diverse patchwork of often contrary policies, not only over time

24

but also – because of the existence of several provincial rather than one central government authority – place. This is evidenced most importantly by diverse approaches towards land taxation and settlement, and the varying extent to which the Indian peasantry was made to suffer the alienation of its means of livelihood. Less drastically the lunacy policies in Madras, Bengal, and Bombay were of different breeds, and subject to continual reorganization. In England, too, the first half of the nineteenth century had yet to produce any unified treatment of the mentally ill. This was still the period of *laissez-faire* with its mixed blessing of experiments and individual initiatives in the absence of restrictions by the state on the one hand, and of rampant abuse of the mentally ill due to lack of public control on the other. Neither in England nor in British India can we therefore assume the existence of a 'policy' in any coherent sense.

Nevertheless, some features were characteristic of all the European asylums in India – most derived from Great Britain, but some were more or less specific to the colonial version of British mental health policy. One such 'typically colonial' feature was the extent to which the colonial state controlled and intervened in the setting up and running of mental institutions. This is not to say that state control was by any means as centrally organized and all-encompassing as in, say, France which has been described as the harbinger of the 'great confinement' in reference to the tendency of the mergent capitalist state to institutionalize the deviant strata of society. What the suggestion of an interventionist stance by the colonial state does imply, though, is that lunacy policy in India, whilst firmly rooted in the more temperate Anglo-Saxon tradition and insular idiosyncrasies, was not simply a poor imitation of English whims and social developments, but rather a colonial hybrid which was allowed to grow somewhat more luxuriant under tropical 'hothouse' conditions.

What then were British officialdom's measures towards the European mentally ill in India? In Madras first attempts towards the clarification of authority structures in the administration of the asylum, and rules about the extent to which it was subject to medical as well as government control, had been made as early as 1808.[22] Similarly, the Bombay authorities made provision for the maintenance in the asylum of both military and civil employees of the Company (and even, from 1801 onwards, for individuals unconnected with it).[23] Rules for the internal management and public control of asylums were drawn up in 1801. In Bengal the situation was less clear – largely due to the fact that here the only asylum for Europeans was left in private hands until almost the time of the Indian revolt of 1857. But even in Bengal the policy of regularly shipping inmates back to Europe was implemented from 1818 onwards, and some control, however restricted, was exercised over the asylum proprietors' regime of management and their admission and discharge practices. Long before that date, from 1788 onwards, lunatics of all sorts – albeit mostly those of purely European origin – were routinely admitted to the province's asylum, and the expense for their maintenance was charged to the exchequer's accounts.[24] Moreover, due to the existence of medical boards vested with the immediate responsibility for the provinces' medical affairs and institutions, a system of public inspection had been more or less successfully in place in India from the late eighteenth century onwards, thus preceding the setting up of public watchdogs such as the 'commissioners in lunacy' in England by about half a century.

From today's stand-point it may well be held that measures such as the clarification of authority structures, and the enforcement of rules about the relative place of medical as well as government control in the management of asylums are very mundane and uncontroversial matters which would characterize *any* organization rather than providing evidence of features specific to colonial lunacy policy at the time. After all, it could be argued, the least a state or state-like organization would do, was to provide and enforce the framework of rules within which institutions are to operate. However, if in the particular case of colonial lunacy policy the extent of the state's control is contrasted with policies 'at home' in England, things look quite different. The Company certainly practised interventionism at a time when reformers in England were still unsuccessfully campaigning for it.

The existence of routinized practices, regular inspection and more or less detailed regulations does, of course, not imply that in practice things went according to the book. Rather, mismanagement, corruption, and petty disputes were uncovered on several occasions. Corrupt practices and mediocre performance were, however, typical not only of people involved in lunacy, but of all departments of government. The more important point here is that, notwithstanding petty scandals, the East India Company officially took charge of insane European subjects in India at a time when in England and Wales the central state's liability for the secure custody and medical treatment of the mentally ill was still under discussion and was not realized until 1845. This important difference certainly owes much to a strong Scottish element amongst colonial administrators which advanced a typical Scottish brand of humanitarianism and state intervention. It is, however, not least due to the peculiar nature of colonial rule in the East Indies itself.

It had been towards the late eighteenth century that the East India Company's administration of Indian affairs was gradually consolidated, and the Company itself subjected to scrutiny by the British parliament through a board of control. Unlike in earlier days there was to be no more trade without complementary civil and military measures. Military supremacy would ensure that British footholds in India could be upheld, by force if necessary. Civil administration would not only be instrumental, as Grant argued, in diffusing 'the light and benign influence of the truth, the blessings of well-regulated society, the improvement and comforts of active industry' among Indian peoples who had 'long sunk in darkness, vice and misery', but it would also guarantee the smooth functioning of small – albeit steadily enlarging – pockets of European settlements under an 'alien sky' and amongst an allegedly backward people.[25] With the passing of Pitt's India Act and the Cornwallis Reforms, and finally the abolition of the Company's trade monopolies in the East (in 1813 for China, and in 1833 for India) the shift from commerce to government was nearly accomplished.

Consequently the Company's authorities in India and England gradually assumed the function of a 'pseudo-state' with a retinue of administrators, the forerunners of the 'heaven-born' members of the later civil service. The governors of Madras, Bombay, and Bengal met regularly with their councils to discuss and decide on the various departments' policy matters, and conveyed their minutes to London to await sanction by the court of directors. The court of directors in its function as the Company's governing body in turn despatched its decisions to India, after having them approved by the board of control. These multiple levels of administration resulted in tension amongst officials at various points in the hierarchy. The subordination of this administration to the British state proper was maintained by the dependence of the renewal of the Company's royal charter every twenty years on the findings of a select committee specially installed to investigate the administration of East Indian affairs.

Public opinion and parliament's approval were therefore decisive factors for the survival of 'John Company's' rule in India. Areas of public concern such as the fate of lunatics tended to attract attention and criticism. After all, the early nineteenth century was the period of humanitarian campaigns and social reforms, when celebrities such as William Wilberforce and Sir A. Halliday roused middle-class public opinion in support of causes like the plight of slaves and the care for the destitute and mentally ill in Britain and abroad. The Company's court of directors in London therefore was in principle desirous that the local governments in India introduced without delay the recommendations of select committees on lunacy – especially if the envisaged reforms did not constitute any additional major expense.

The 1815/16 select committee on the better regulation of madhouses in England was the most influential in that respect. It had originally been set up with the aim of controlling the infamous practice of private asylum owners of making the most of a 'free market in lunatics' which then flourished mainly on account of the lack of public establishments for pauper lunatics. A pressure group of philanthropists aimed at revealing and preventing gross abuses such as came to light in an inquiry when an emaciated James Norris had been found chained to the wall in a pitiful state in Bethlem Hospital. During the course of the investigation strong evidence was provided of the 'filth, neglect and unthinking brutality' found to be typical of lower-class establishments.[26] There was no indication that up-market establishments which provided for a selected number of well-to-do patients suffered from defects even remotely comparable to those endemic to pauper asylums. Abhorrent conditions were the doubtful privilege of the poor, and one that was basically ignored by the wealthy. As Chadwick expressed it, the facts were 'as strange' to the wealthier classes 'as if related to foreigners or the natives of an unknown country'.[27]

Despite the conclusive evidence which pointed at the necessity for 'better care to be taken of insane persons', the remedial measures proposed by the committee were not legally enforced.[28] The condition of lunatics in England therefore experienced as little improvement as it had following the previous select committee of 1808, when the erection of publicly funded county asylums was advised but not made compulsory. None of the 1815/16 Committee's proposals, such as the creation of especially designed, publicly financed and controlled county asylums, was implemented in England until 1845. In India in contrast, the main core of improvements envisaged by the committees of 1808 and 1815/16 had been realized by the first two decades of the nineteenth century. (The presence at the Company's London end of reformist officials necessarily facilitated this process.)

The abolition in 1817 of the practice of contracting-out the supply of asylum provisions to private entrepreneurs or medical officers is but one example. The advocacy in 1820 of a regime of 'non-restraint' is another. And last but not least, long before the committee of 1808 would recommend the construction of a public asylum in each of England's counties, a government asylum existed in Bengal (albeit only until 1821) that admitted the mentally ill of all social classes. Further government asylums for Europeans in addition to separate public institutions for Indians were opened during the first two decades of the nineteenth century in Bombay and Madras. And what is more, and very much in contrast to asylums in England, both the institutions for Indians and those for Europeans were subject to public control, regardless of whether they were in private hands (like the Calcutta asylum from 1821 to 1856) or state owned (like the asylums in Bombay and Madras). They had in theory to be visited regularly by a board of inspectors, and the superintendent, who had to be a medical professional or at least have routine medical assistance, was obliged to keep registers and case books. On special occasions visitors such as the governor-general, and 'some of the highest authorities of Government'[29] would be shown round on the premises, so that the general impression prevailed that the British in India were at least as humanitarian as, if not 'much further advanced than England'.[30]

In 1851 the London authorities made their wish explicit that 'those valuable improvements in the treatment of Lunatics which have been introduced into European Asylums should, as far as possible, be made available for the benefit of the same unhappy class in India'. This statement sums up the Company's official stance (and, to a somewhat more limited extent, the prevalent practice) towards European lunatics in the East.[31] The ruling classes in India, it appears, were eager to convey the image of an elite which was devoted to the welfare of its own and its subject peoples. Such an image was as important for the preservation of the expatriate's self-perception of being a superior and enlightened race amongst 'brutes' as it was for the British public's conviction that British colonial rule was a blessing for alien peoples.

Exposure of grievances like those endured by James Norris in London would have been unpalatable to the British and the expatriate community had it occurred in Calcutta. That is not to say that abuse of lunatics did not exist in British India. To the contrary, the government of Bengal, for example, had been alerted by reports of the 'numerous deaths' which occurred in some of the province's asylums due to insufficient institutional provision. It consequently installed a committee to inquire into the 'state and internal management of lunatic asylums'.[32] Circumstances very much akin to those in the worst kind of lower-class institutions in England were revealed, and condemned by the authorities.[33] The crucial point was, however, that gross abuse was only detected (and rarely acted upon wholly successfully) in the treatment of *Indians.* Notwithstanding the fact that the mortality of European second-class patients in the Bengal asylum, for example, had been nearly double that of the first class (reflecting the class-specific death-rates of the European community in India as a whole), Europeans seem to have enjoyed throughout the early part of the century conditions very much superior to those prevalent in the various districts' 'native lunatic asylums' and the Bombay and Madras asylums' 'native wings'.[34] If the humanitarian image of the British had to suffer somewhat, then it was in regard to the treatment of the Indian rather than the European mentally ill.

Whilst abuse of inmates and mismanagement of asylums was largely confined to the 'native' asylum sector, malpractice was a phenomenon deeply embedded in almost all government departments. Corruptive practices not only had adverse effects on government finances but were in many cases also detrimental to patients' health and welfare. A typical and most consequential case was that of asylum and hospital contracts.

Ever since the establishment of a lunatic asylum in Bengal some time prior to 1787, food provision, clothing, and bedding were supplied by a private contractor, typically the asylum owner or medical officer on duty in the institution. This practice and with it the grounded suspicion of large-scale embezzlement was well known amongst British officialdom in India. In hospitals, too, contractors had for decades made large profits by pocketing money for provision which had never reached patients. It had even been found that 'on some occasions at least the health and life of the Soldier was sacrificed to the avarice of the Surgeon'.[35]

Despite the authorities' familiarity with such 'very great abuses', not much was done to enforce more stringent regulations. Similarly, for nearly three decades no steps had been taken to change lunatic asylums' supply system. The reason for this omission was partly to be blamed on ignorance or indifference, but it had also a personal dimension that was ever-present among government officials within the restricted circle of polite society in British India. Public servants wined and dined with the very same officers whose source of additional income they would eliminate in case changes in public administration were suggested at council meetings. Even *griffins* or newcomers who may at times have arrived in the East with the best intention at some future point to rectify ills and better the ways in which the Company's affairs were being administered, found it difficult to elevate themselves above the common practice of profiteering and favouritism. They after all had to nurture social contacts if they did not want to risk exclusion from social entertainments and the looming danger of loneliness and depression.

Charles Metcalfe, for example, who, in a romantic fashion regarded politics to be the 'most noble of professions' arrived in Calcutta in 1801.[36] Of the few events noteworthy enough to be entered in his diary during the first few weeks in town, were regular visits for dinner at 'Dr Dick's'.[37] Dick was the owner of the lunatic asylum and a well-known and influential medical practitioner with extensive private practice. No newcomer, however convinced of the heroic role of colonial politics, would have dined with ease at Dick's, had he contemplated officially raising any serious allusion to the doubtful nature of some of his host's income sources.

There were however also limits to the extent to which malpractice could be condoned by local public servants for

31

prolonged periods of time. This limit was to a large extent set by the increasing scrutiny of the Company's officials in London. It so happened that in 1816 the examiner in the Company's London office smelt a rat of potential corruption. Being as a Londoner less likely to be involved in Calcutta's life after hours, he demanded a change of system.[38] It was recommended that the commissariate was to supply the asylum's necessities against bills countersigned and checked by the medical board. Furthermore, the medical officer in charge of asylum inmates was no longer allowed to pursue additional occupations. Such attentiveness to details of asylum administration had been sparked off partly by public and parliamentary concern for lunatics in England which peaked in 1815. It took however some time before government policy to curb corruptive practices was implemented thoroughly enough at all levels of asylum administration to be beyond public criticism – let alone, to have a positive effect on inmates' daily life. After all, changes in regulations alone could not guarantee improvements.

The extent to which any administrative reform would work on the spot was of course very much dependent on whether officers right down the hierarchy carried out with diligence their superiors' orders and recommendations. The Company's employment practices, however, did not encourage asylum personnel to see their job as a career rather than as an opportunity for additional earnings. Although salaries were kept on a comparatively high level, promotion prospects were erratic and unsatisfying to many. Further, the position of asylum superintendent was usually but one among several charges of a medical officer – and one that did not enjoy any particular kudos. It was only towards the end of the Company's rule, in the late 1850s, that double-incomes, and corruption by government employees more generally, came to an end.

Despite the prevalence of corruption and the deterioration of provision towards the middle of the nineteenth century, the Company could claim that it had developed for its European lunatics a system of care, if not as Sir A. Halliday proclaimed over-enthusiastically, 'much further advanced', at least very much the equal of the more salubrious institutions in the British Isles. It was to a great extent public opinion in England and parliament's scrutiny of civil administration in the East that helped to detect petty embezzlement and spurred reforms in lunacy provision. It remains to be assessed how such reforms were implemented and tailored to the specific needs of colonial rule. One conspicuous point here is that officials were prepared to pursue interventionist policies in the colony whilst reluctance to promote a centralized and costly public health policy was evident in Britain. Even the great advocates of state intervention, James and John Stuart Mill, were in a critical note characterized by a Calcutta newspaper as 'demagogues at home' and 'despots abroad'.[39] It was alleged that they judged 'Indian questions by rules and standards the very opposite of those they employ to decide all other questions whatever'.

What was it that made civil servants opt for an interventionist style of government abroad whilst playing safe and liberal at home even in areas of policy making as marginal as lunacy policy? Officials in India worked, of course, in a completely different setting. The changing emphasis in colonial administration from, say, Hastings' injunction to 'adapt our Regulations to the Manners and Understanding of the People'[40] to that of a Macaulay who wished to raise 'a class of persons Indian in colour and blood, but English in tastes, in opinions, in morals, and in intellect'[41] accounted to a great extent for strict state control. Such control was to be exerted not only over the Indian subject people but also over the European communities who were after all expected to provide the good example to which Indians were expected to aspire. Further, there was the widespread belief in the civilizing mission which not only justified centralization but also nurtured reformist measures that were as yet unprecedented under the more inert circumstances in England. India appealed to post-Enlightenment ideologues who saw their chance, as Wilberforce succinctly expressed it, 'to strike our roots into the soil by the gradual introduction and establishment of our own principles and opinions; of our laws, institutions, and manners'.[42] Western vanguard ideologies and political practices were in fact transplanted to the East, but – and here it is important to qualify Wilberforce's emphatic statement somewhat – they were trimmed to better fit the very different conditions in the colony.

The sick, the poor, and the mad

There were yet other characteristics at work, relating to the social make-up of European colonial society itself, which encouraged, if not necessitated state control. The British – and in particular those of the lower classes – had found a peculiar freedom in India. The freedom from a sense of belonging to the place where they spent a considerable span of time of their working lives, and, in most cases, freedom from family ties and from the guardians of the poor. In the case of military servants, army hierarchy and regimental pride at times helped to create but (because of nationalism and religious quarrels) did not ensure a communal spirit or *esprit de corps*. Among civilians, cohesive tendencies and community spirit were kept alive by the continuous struggle to maintain separation from an unfamiliar Indian environment. Despite the ruling elite's endeavours to recreate English social life in the East and to cling together in small exclusive social circles, the European community was largely devoid, if not of family support, then, in the case of the lower classes certainly of parochial relief. There were no overseers of the poor who were by force of custom or law responsible for the care of European down-and-outs.

Polite society in places like Calcutta, Madras, or Bombay did make some effort to raise money for institutions such as orphanages, sailors' homes and hospitals for the poor. Lushington's account of 1824 of Calcutta's missionary and charitable institutions provides evidence of such private relief initiatives. The European community in Madras, too, had gained fame for its initiation of social relief projects, while Europeans in Bombay were at pains to compete with the local Parsi community, who had a strong tradition of charity.

The funds raised by subscriptions and collections were, however, never sufficient to provide for the steadily increasing number of poor whites who tended to take to the streets and to begging. Nor could funds invested in poor relief help to clear the European quarters in built-up areas of destitute 'natives', and ameliorate to even the smallest extent the living conditions of the Indian poor. Absence of parish relief and the limitations of private charity left the Company to fill the remaining gap. It certainly did so in the case of the European mentally ill. The provincial governments responded in a less unitary and organized way to other areas of social welfare and public health, in particular to the relief of lower-class Europeans.

The Company's commercially more successful days of penny-pinching budgets had not yet long enough passed to allow it to be indifferent to the cost of social relief measures – in particular as it became aware of the magnitude of the problem. The number of European vagrants, deserters, prostitutes, and of what would nowadays be labelled the 'unemployed poor', rose steadily during the course of the early nineteenth century. On the Indian side the misery of the peasantry, of landless labourers, and of the Indian version of the 'lumpenproletariat' became more manifest once British rule had been firmly established. Where officials had previously assumed that a few hospitals, dispensaries, asylums, and jails here and there would be enough to provide both Indians and Europeans with the 'blessings of well-regulated society', they gradually came to realise that they had miscalculated.[43] The Company consequently emphasized the limitations weighing down upon its public and health departments and tried to shift responsibility for social welfare to the inhabitants of the various municipalities whenever possible. In 1857 the Court of Directors re-asserted that whilst local governments would be authorized to provide medicine and to meet one quarter of the maintenance cost for hospitals and dispensaries, it was the 'wealthier classes' who were 'responsible' for their establishment in the first place.[44]

There was yet one other area for which the Company had customarily assumed responsibility: the medical care of military and naval servants. The upkeep of soldiers and sailors was not only strategically vital but also costly. The royal commission on the sanitary state of the army in India did not beat about the bush in its report of 1863: 'The value of a man who, with all his arms, costs the country £100 a year is considerable, and either the loss of his life, of his health, or of his efficiency, is not to be lightly regarded'.[45] The preservation of soldiers' health and consequently of their fighting power was an important means of making sure that the cost of their recruitment and outfitting would be redeemed.

Atrocious as the state of the health of the soldiery in the East was during the early part of the nineteenth century (with a mortality rate for the rank and file 82 per cent higher than that for officers), there was at least some medical treatment available.[46] Once outside the tight net of the military, former soldiers were no longer entitled to any government support. Civilians could usually not count on medical or social relief, unless they constituted an immediate threat or nuisance to the European community (in which case they were most likely to be locked up in jail or, in the case of contagious diseases, subjected to isolation and in later years inoculation and vaccination). The chronically ill or those suffering from the usual range of tropical diseases, both European and Indian, usually had to fend for themselves. Sickness, the great companion of British daily life in India, was one eventuality for which there was scant and substandard support in the early nineteenth century, if the afflicted happened to be a civilian of Indian or lower-class European extraction.

The European middle-turned-ruling-class was, despite the institutional veneer of Georgian and Victorian humani- tarianism, not particularly sensitive to the plight of the unfortunate and sick amongst its own – unless they were of like rank. The Bengal General Hospital, for example, was meant for the reception of Europeans – but only those of the better classes. There was one occasion though on which it would open its doors to the sick poor: when an epidemic struck. Once it had passed, and the authorities were sure that vagabonding Europeans would no longer endanger the community at large, admission to the institution would again be restricted. In 1835, for example, superior medical officers reminded government of the necessity to take steps to prevent municipal authorities from sending paupers into the General Hospital. This institution, they insisted, was never meant for the reception of lower-class Europeans, and only extraordinary circumstances such as those prevailing during the recent plague epidemic would legitimate a diversion from the established rule.[47]

Sick Europeans of the 'lowly' kind had to make do at best with most unimpressive and badly equipped premises: the few small local police hospitals that existed in the major cities. The institutions' name already gives their nature and intent away. They were meant for the reception of the 'plebs' and owed their inmates mainly to the ever-vigilant eyes of the local police who would pick up diseased paupers. However, not every sick or emaciated and destitute European would be allowed to benefit from medicine, and (often more attractive to the patients) rations of alcoholic spirits and free meals – only those who were by virtue of the nature of their disease and behaviour expected to constitute a nuisance if not threat to the general public. In 1839 for example, the government of India insisted that the few pauper hospitals that existed 'must not be converted into Poor Houses or Mendicant Hospitals'.[48] Only if the hospitals had some spare funds available, could the medical staff at their own discretion provide some relief 'in extreme cases'. The official aim here was clearly to cut down on government expenditure, and to leave responsibility for poor relief with private initiative.

The local governments' stance also exemplifies the endeavour to differentiate amongst the various groups of the poor and to establish who was to 'deserve' government support and specialized institutional treatment. In so doing it echoed a crucial aspect of the English New Poor Law. Any legal equivalent to the English Poor Law was in fact lacking in the East. Yet the provincial authorities experimented with various different measures, which owed much of their ideological content and practicalities to the English blueprint. The way in which they were implemented, however, was adapted to the specific circumstances of colonial rule. The provincial governments in India did not accept any binding legal responsibility for the care of the sick European poor. Neither did the government back home in England.

However, Europeans in India were meant to be visible in public only as a 'formidable' ruling elite, and therefore not in a state of sickness, destitution, madness, or infirmity. They had to be kept out of sight of not only easily offended well-to-do Europeans but also of higher-caste Indians, many of whom had a sense of social precedence and discrimination which was only equalled by the more opinionated among the British. It was this precept of colonial rule – of the maintenance of social distance not only between the races but also among the various classes of European society – which to a great extent accounted for the number of specialized institutions that were (despite the Indian governments' reluctance to provide in-door-relief) gradually established at an early period on either government or private initiative: for the cities' impressive general hospitals and the more inferior police hospitals, for the well-equipped 'higher' orphanages (for officers' and gentlemen's children) and the less welcoming 'lower' orphanages (for children of soldiers), for the treadmills, workhouses, sailors' homes, lock hospitals, and lunatic asylums.

Institutionalization was one way of making people 'invisible' who would otherwise be 'a nuisance and threat in every avenue'.[49] Another was to send them to the hills or back to England. Hill-stations in particular had been thought of by medical practitioners as the ideal place for diseased Europeans to recover from the strains of military and civil duty: the climate and scenic setting were after all said to have resembled parts of Surrey or the Isle of Wight. This expectation proved however to have been ill-conceived, as the hills soon became the exclusive playground of well-to-do civil servants, officers, and business-men. It was not until the mid-nineteenth century that the government each year packed its books and pencils lock, stock, and barrel and moved to the temperate surroundings of Simla, which were much more congenial to the languid British con-stitution than Calcutta. But soon after the first roads had been built, investment in bungalow development started. House and land prices soared as the regular exodus of British India's more prosperous classes was anticipated prior to the onset of the hot season. It became therefore evident by mid-century that if any disadvantaged or sick Europeans were to be welcome in this elitist colonial refuge, it was only the man or woman with less serious afflictions, and certainly not the down-and-out or lunatic.

Only selected groups were seen as fit subjects to benefit from the salubrious climate in the hills. Orphans for example were one such group innocent enough to be tolerated. They were brought up behind closed doors and well sheltered from any dreaded and potentially harmful influence such as the Indian environment. Similarly, convalescent soldiers would be sent to sanatoria in the hills where they were restored to their former fighting selves within the confines of rehabilitation centres and well secluded from both the holidaying public and the temptations of the East. This practice was calculated to work out cheaper than the replacement of troops with new recruits from England.

In regard to other groups (such as the mentally ill and the poor), the authorities' and the public's attitude was much less favourable. The plan for a lunatic hill-station had at least been mooted, though of course not realized. But the notion that a treadmill or workhouse could possibly benefit from the climate of Simla's or Darjeeling's slopes had not even been conceived of. In the plains the location for such institutions as jails, lock-hospitals, asylums and workhouses was carefully selected. The general practice of colonial town planning provides evidence for the desire not only to separate the European quarters from 'native' areas, and, if necessary, to demolish or move Indian markets in order to avoid their proximity to public buildings and private bungalows. It also shows that buildings such as penitentiaries were literally confined to the very margins of the European settlements. In holiday resorts such as the hills, a segregative public works policy could only be expected to be applied even more stringently. Lower-class establishments in the hills would have offended the expatriates' sense of social distance and been contrary to the prevailing attitude towards prowlers and paupers. It was punishment rather than the impact of fresh and salubrious mountain air which was expected to work on people of their kind.

Although they were treated in very different ways, both the destitute and the mentally ill were either to be kept securely within institutions in the plains, or else deported from the colony. Time-expired soldiers as well as people such as European women of 'bad character', vagabonds, and lunatics, were provided with passages back to Europe, where they would be left to their own devices, or in the case of the mentally ill received into 'Pembroke House', the Company's lunatic asylum near London. Deportation was costly, but it guaranteed that social misfits and unproductive elements of society would not only be permanently out of sight but also that they would no longer be a burden on the treasury. Sending the 'rabble' back home to England was more congenial to the social sensitivities of the European community than the establishment of workhouses or sailors' homes in India which would have had an undesirable air of permanency.

As long as the Company's policy of selective immigration control was in force during the earlier decades of the nineteenth century, the number of Europeans of the lower classes could be kept down. So could the cost of repatriation. Times changed however, and so did the social composition of the European community in India. By the 1850s about half of the white population belonged to what could be called 'poor' Europeans. In the face of such large numbers, repatriation was no longer economically viable, nor was the policy of immigration restriction as practicable and successful as originally planned. Deportation of those who were in possession of their wits but of not much else, was consequently carried out in a decreasingly routinized way. The European community was slowly though reluctantly forced to come to terms with the fact that even under the formidable rule of the Raj there could be no European elite without the lower orders of their own kind. The way those higher up the social and racial hierarchy responded was by increased stringency of social segregation and observance of rules of precedence which startled even class-conscious society in the clubs and tea-rooms in England.

The early nineteenth-century practice of repatriating those among the mentally ill who did not recover within a year in the European asylums in India certainly owed much to the Company's protectionist immigration policy and to a general and widespread distaste for lower-class and socially deviant people. Lunacy policy as a whole was strongly conditioned by the ambition to discipline and control, and to make the lower strata of the European community in particular fit in with the behavioural demands seen to be appropriate to a ruling elite. It was however also – albeit only until the middle of the century – the velvet glove of measures for the control and relief of Europeans in India. Unlike mendicants and vagrants, the mentally ill were not punished for their state. On the contrary, lunatics had to be treated with 'great care and attention', whilst institutions for the poor *aimed* at providing undesirable conditions for its inmates.[50]

Conditions in the European asylum were certainly not as bad as in the workhouse and jail. This is however not to say that Europeans' madness in India was perceived and treated in an unprejudiced way. The authorities were just as keen to get lunatics off the cities' avenues and off the account books as they were to get rid of the sick and poor. Further, contact with the mad, or even only the knowledge of their presence close by, was not appreciated – as evidenced in the case of Lady Grey, who pressed the Bengal government to disembark a batch of lunatics from the vessel in which she was supposed to sail home in 1833.[51] In a similar vein, distinguished citizens of Madras formed a pressure group in order to petition government to abandon the plan to build an asylum in the midst of a recently 'gentrified' suburb which, they argued, would make the area undesirable for Europeans, bringing property prices down.[52] In Bombay the authorities had the insane conveniently separated and literally 'insulated' from the general population by allocating them land on the island and later peninsula of Salzette.

Notwithstanding a certain amount of prejudice, what then made government authorities in early nineteenth-century India more inclined to view the plight of the mentally ill in a somewhat less unfavourable light than that of the poor and destitute generally? Basically, they were disposed to accept the former as an unfortunate mishap rather than as the result of individual malice, self-inflicted misfortune, or simple lack of willpower. Madness was widely seen to be 'a calamity the heaviest which can well befall a rational and responsible being'.[53] To a great extent it was the expatriate's problem in coming to grips with life under unfamiliar circumstances, or, as it was then called, with exposure to the Indian environment, to the tropical sun, or indulgence in vice and alcohol, that was blamed for derangement in Europeans. As long as the alien environment and the temptations of the East rather than personal predisposition or lack of self-control were found to be responsible for Europeans' mental state, community and patriotic spirit were revived and sympathy rather than blame was bestowed on the sufferers.

The less censorious attitude towards the mentally ill was to a large extent the result of the fact that madness unlike destitution crossed barriers of social class. It was true that great fortunes could be as easily lost in the East as they were at times gained. But rarely would a gentleman fall victim to destitution and end up in the city's gutters. Madness in contrast could reduce any bright officer's or government servant's intelligent conversation to inchoate babble. Ever since the opening of lunatic asylums in India they had been occupied by inmates of all social classes. As a consequence, the authorities did not measure lunacy against the same yardstick of culpability as destitution and mendicancy. The presence of higher-class patients in the provincial asylums therefore ensured to a great extent that the European asylum sector would (despite its function within colonial society as a whole of ensuring peace and order) not yet be intrinsically linked with the policy towards paupers.

The preferential treatment of European lunatics was however not beyond criticism. Critics had voiced their disapproval of what they considered to be highly exaggerated provision for the mentally ill ever since government had made asylums open their doors and accounts to regular inspection. Every now and then inmates were downgraded from first to second class, or wealthy relatives asked to pay for the maintenance of their family members in the asylum. Criticism, however, focused mainly on the high cost of asylum provision. The more general question of whether the local governments in

India ought to be responsible at all for the maintenance of European lunatics there and on arrival back home in England was not confronted until 1852. Then the sympathetic policy towards the European mentally ill came as close to being questioned in principle as it ever could come under colonial rule. By that time the three asylums for Europeans in India were hopelessly overcrowded, conditions had deteriorated because of the lack of funds available for staffing, refurbishment, and reconstruction, and, what is more, the reorganization of the civil administration's medical department was under way.

It was not merely the principle of segregating the mad from other social groups, such as the sick, the poor, and destitute, and treating them in a comparatively favourable way, that was under scrutiny: the still broader question was raised why government should do more 'for insane East Indians, or other Christians, or people of European habits, than it does for its Native Hindoo and Mahomedan subjects when in the same lamentable condition'.[54] The exception, or 'the only speciality', it was argued by Bengal government officials, were Europeans, and in particular 'those of the lower ranks' and in government employ. They should as hitherto be maintained out of public funds. However, whilst it was morally right to assume a certain responsibility for the mentally ill, government was not legally obliged to do so, and in particular not to the extent, nay extravagance, with which it had looked after the European mad.

Such argumentation went down well in the Bengal council chambers which were between 1848 and 1856 presided over by Lord Dalhousie. He was not inclined to make do with minor changes in the supervision of Calcutta's private, and the other two presidencies' public asylums, or with minor cuts in maintenance rates. He had the medical service reorganized in 1856 and put European lunatic asylums on an administrative footing similar to that of county asylums in England, except that they also made separate provision for first-class patients. The period of sporadic measures and of relatively sympathetic government responses towards the lower-class insane had come to an end. The stern spirit of centrally administered public institutions and of clearly circumscribed regulations came to drive out the asylums' hitherto more permissive arrangements.

Administrative reforms and legal provision

Lord Dalhousie's reforms certainly initiated a period of significant change in the policy towards the insane in India. It had been long overdue. In Bengal the medical authorities had already in the 1830s advocated a change in the asylum's system of management. They wanted the then privately owned asylum to be taken over by government and the medical board to be vested with the exclusive authority to manage and control institutional affairs. Further, improvements in asylum conditions had been suggested in Madras and Bombay since the number of institutionalized lunatics there had increased significantly from about the late 1830s and early 1840s onwards. In both places the attempted amelioration of overcrowding by regular extensions and other patching-up efforts was no longer sufficient.

On the grounds of numbers alone then, lunacy provision had necessarily gained a higher profile in the treasury's accounts and was increasingly liable to government scrutiny. Yet neither the Company's court of directors nor the governments in India considered an extension of European asylums and the concomitant increase in funds to be feasible. On the contrary. The authorities were determined to cut down on the expense of the ever-growing 'general department'. Leaving conditions to deteriorate further was however no longer a viable solution, as consequential effects from select committees preceding the passing of the trend-setting lunacy acts of 1842 and 1845 in England were already in the offing. The European public could soon be expected to turn their attention to the plight of the insane in India and to what might well be interpreted as conditions very much inferior to those existing in England.

In fact a Dr G.A. Berwick offered in 1847 his services to the Bengal government in an attempt to improve mental institutions in India and to put them on a footing comparable to what he had seen in the more advanced amongst British asylums. His suggestion contained however not only what the province's medical board called 'the crude and incongruous scheme of assembling Europeans and Natives in one Establishment' for the sake of better surveillance (which was anathema to the Europeans in India as much as to the Hindu and Muslim community), but of making ample provision for the Indian insane, the number of which he anticipated to rise

43

(which was contrary to the authorities' austere financial policy).[55] Berwick's plan was consequently shelved.

Nevertheless, public opinion was in the process of changing – shifting from the early enthusiasm of a Sir A. Halliday who considered asylums in India as superior to English institutions, to the more gloomy picture of colonial institutions as dank 'dungeons' towards the middle of the century. In Bombay the asylum superintendent had to firmly refute allegations in 1852 by an anonymous writer in one of the town's newsletters that the asylum was a 'disgrace to the British government and name'.[56] And in 1854 Dr J. Macpherson complained that 'the Asylums now in existence in India . . . have, some of them at least, all the appearance of jails'.[57] This significant change of opinion on the state of India's asylums certainly owed much to earlier naive overstatement and the ambition to play off policy makers and philanthropists in the British Isles against the Company's administrators in order to speed up reforms. It is however also indicative of an actual worsening of asylum conditions in India because of the governments' restrictions on public spending in a period of continual increase in patients' numbers. As governor Falkland expressed it: 'under the present financial embarrassment before we can attend to the dictates of humanity it becomes our duty to provide for the security of the people'.[58]

What then *were* the options open to the Company and the executive governments in India in the 1850s? They could either maintain the status quo (thereby risking accusations of neglect and mismanagement), or extend existing provision (bringing on the auditor-general's disapproval), or else they could re-organize the whole system from its roots. The latter was exactly what was achieved during Dalhousie's term of office and the remaining two years before the Company ceased to be in charge of the administration of British India. To begin with, the private trade in lunacy and consequently the potential for financial extravagance and corruption that persisted in Bengal until 1856 was done away with, and government took over the management of the province's lunatics. At the same time any significant future increase in the cost of asylum provision arising from an increase in the number of inmates was pre-empted by a drastic reduction in all but first-class patients' maintenance rates. And last but not least the decision-making process was considerably simplified and the potential for

44

friction among government servants reduced by investing a single superintending surgeon with the control of each province's medical institutions.

Most significantly, however, a package of new laws was devised that aimed at unifying lunacy provision in India, and at integrating English and Indian regulations. The Indian Lunatic Asylum Act, for example, was one of three acts passed by the legislative council of India in 1858 with the explicit aim of bringing the legal situation in India in line with that in Britain. It provided a uniform legal basis for the establishment of public lunatic asylums by the executive governments of each province, and aimed at preventing one of the threats most dreaded by the Victorians: wrongful confinement. At the same time it allowed for the maintenance within public institutions of lunatics who were neglected or treated cruelly by their relatives or friends.

The act's main purpose was certainly (like its English model) to facilitate the growth of publicly funded and controlled asylums in place of privately owned institutions – an important step in that it accorded well with the general tendency towards the consolidation and centralization of the colonial state. Special concessions were however made to Indian circumstances. The most important was that the erection of asylums was made optional rather than compulsory. In so doing the act reflected the authorities' general conviction that whilst intervention by the colonial state in civil affairs was seen as necessary, the *specifica differentia* of colonial administration in the various parts of British India was bound to impede any imposition of uniform requirements.

The Indian Lunatic Asylum Act also empowered the executive governments to grant licences for private asylums. This provision may at first sight appear contrary to the tendency in England and the very intent of the act to restrict the private 'trade in lunacy' in favour of public institutions. Previous experience in Bengal, too, had shown that confining public patients in a private asylum was bound to lead to sometimes irreconcilable conflict between proprietor and medical authorities. The key to the act's seemingly incongruent provision lies with the fact that both in England and India public institutions possessed an ambivalent image. Persons of all ranks and walks of life were to be admitted into public asylums. In the language of the law this meant that 'every darogah or district police officer' had to send to the magistrate 'all persons found wandering at large . . . who are deemed to be lunatics, and all persons believed to be dangerous by reason of lunacy'.[59] What in fact the Indian act provided for was the possibility of two separate types of institution: one (public) for paupers and lower-class people, and one (private) for upper class lunatics. In so doing it reflected (if only as an option) the tendency of English developments in consequence of the passing of the Lunatics Act – namely the retention of private houses for the rich.

The acts of 1858 contained material that had in England been considered as most controversial. The concern about the prevention of wrongful confinement and the preservation of individual freedom, for example, which had been occasioned by the concomitant demand for the state to evolve an interventionist stance, had been a typical matter of contention for many decades. Despite this, the discussion preceding the passing of the Indian acts was short and uncontroversial. After all, recourse was had to laws which had already been enforced in England, and which were at the time of their application in India considered to be sufficiently comprehensive and humanitarian.[60] At the same time the new regulations were open to interpretation within the various conditions in which administrators found themselves. With the enactments of 1858 (which were in slightly amended forms to be in force until 1912), the period of patchy legal provision and relative variety of approaches towards the management of the mad came to an end. From this time on one can speak of a 'system' of asylum provision in British India. What the law provided for was basically a system that was structurally akin to that extant in the British Isles, adapted to Indian circumstances.

Prior to the momentous enactments of 1858, legal provision had been made in 1849 and 1851 for a special group among the insane – 'criminal' lunatics: those amongst the mentally ill who had committed a violent act that would under ordinary circumstances have been punishable under the penal law. The association between states of 'unsoundness of mind' and the law was not peculiar to colonial rule alone, nor was it typical only of Anglo-Saxon legislation. Irrespective of the state of the law, criminal lunatics had been subject to greater public apprehension than the mentally ill in general. This was not so much because of the often reasonable fear that they might repeat a violent action, but because it was frequently in question whether a verdict of 'unsoundness of mind' was legitimate. Shamming was after all suspected to be common practice among military servants. Insanity in particular was feigned as a last recourse by many a soldier tired of military duty in the East and unable to buy himself out of the service. The common view was that lunatics could not be held responsible for their actions, and that they should be released once their mental derangement had subsided. From 1849 onwards and even more so from 1851 when the legal situation was clearly circumscribed, early discharge would however no longer be guaranteed, as criminal lunatics had to be transferred to the jail in order to serve the full sentence in case they recovered from the mental affliction prior to the end of their term.

There were however quite a few cases, particularly in the military and navy in which a verdict of 'unsoundness of mind' was considered (mistakenly or not) a softer option than the usual disciplinary punishment for insubordination, desertion, or violence. The first half of the nineteenth century was after all the period when discipline among European troops and sailors was frequently enforced by means of the loathed cat-o'-nine-tails and by execution. 'I saw so many flogged', wrote a grenadier after about a decade's service in the East, 'that I was heartily tired of soldiering'.[61] Witnessing for example within one month the execution of a comrade who had been found guilty of 'striking the Surgeon . . . with his shut fist' and of two others from similar offences, he concluded that 'such scenes . . . only tend to make the soldier loathe instead of honouring his profession'.

Being declared insane was also perceived by some desperate to see the last of soldiering as a way out of life-long military service that was only reduced to between seven and twenty-one years during times of war in order to attract a greater number of recruits. Service in the Victorian army was generally acknowledged to be an extremely stressful trade. The recommendation, published in *The Times* in 1858, that 'if a man is anxious to get rid of his life without having recourse to measures of direct suicide, the most honourable way to obtain this desirable end is to enter as a private' in a British regiment, was a sarcastic expression of this. Given the unsalubrious aspects of military life, lunacy appealed to quite a few as an alternative to the madness of service in the East. Not only simple soldiers or sailors resorted to working their ticket in this way. Officers, too, sometimes made the most of the law's insanity clause.

The verdict of 'unsoundness of mind' and its medico-legal implications had in England been subject to controversy throughout the century. Similarly, when the legislative council of India was in the process of framing the new 1849 act aimed at integrating English with Indian rules, and in particular at ensuring that a defendant could no longer 'on a Medical Officer's opinion differing from that recorded on the trial be let loose on society', arguments against the insanity clause were advanced.[62] Drinkwater Bethune, the president of the Indian law commission, for example, believed that the plea of lunacy should be disallowed and that it should be left to the 'prerogative of mercy' to pardon those few 'unhappy persons' who were really free from guilt. He was against framing the law in India in accordance with English law as he considered the latter in its practical application 'far from being in a clear and satisfactory state'.

To make his point, Bethune cited the anecdote of the 'notorious Jonathan Martin' who had set fire to York Cathedral, suggesting that the plea of insanity was then widely discussed by patients in the asylums and that the saying was much in their mouths 'You know they cannot hang him for he is mad'.[63] Basically his Honour considered English law to be too 'tender', pointing at 'the shocking acquittals which have been multiplied lately in England'. He believed that it was preferable by far to deter people from giving 'free vent to their passions' than doing justice to what he considered to be a merely theoretical legal objection: the alleged danger of making those very few who were not able to control their actions accountable for them. In this he was supported by Lord Dalhousie, who shared the opinion that the plea of insanity served in the majority of cases those who knew that they would from their supposed or actual lunacy escape punishment. The governor-general succinctly summarized his point: 'As long as he knows he is doing a wrong, no matter whether he is urged to do it by [diseased] workings of his brain or not, he should in my opinion suffer the penalty of that wrong.'[64]

Despite such strong objection at the highest level of government in India, provisions for the criminal insane were finally made. The draft act was (with but few formal changes)

assented to by the governor-general in December 1848. Both he
and the law commissioner were very well aware that although
criminal lunacy constituted a difficult medico-legal problem,
their view was not consistent with 'general opinion' in England
and would therefore be 'shared by very few'.[65] Bethune rightly
assumed that even if deterrent regulations were passed by the
council in India (which he very much doubted), they would be
vetoed by the Company's court in England. What is more, it was
not considered right that, as Dalhousie put it, the local
government should legislate 'in principles which are so much
beyond the present standard of the law at home'.[66] To that
judgement Bethune could not but agree, as he also maintained
– albeit less successfully – in regard to the Indian penal code in
general a rather orthodox position that closely followed English
enactments. And last but not least lunacy provision had not a
high enough profile for government in India to induce
authorities such as the law commissioner and the governor-
general to go against 'general opinion' in pursuit of measures
they would personally have preferred.

Though Bethune and Dalhousie considered the criminal
lunatics law as too 'tender', the practical consequences for the
insane themselves were anything but a reason for rejoicing.
Together with Dalhousie's other reforms of the asylum sector,
the criminal lunacy legislation helped to enforce a strict system
of segregation and discrimination. Criminal lunatics were kept
separate from other asylum inmates and were not usually
allowed to partake in the few amusements and privileges
granted to them. It is true that the verdict of 'not guilty on
account of unsoundness of mind' could be abused. Conversely,
the fate of a person who was detained for life in the asylum or
jail 'even though there be a restoration to reason' could by the
standards of neither liberal nor conservative opinion really be
considered fortunate when the ever more parsimonious
institutional conditions that were enforced towards the middle
of the century for all but first-class patients are taken into
account.

The enactments of 1849 and 1851 were considered by district
judges in India to be most important milestones in the
consolidation of an hitherto open legal situation. With the act
of 1849 the authority in the criminal courts necessary for the
detention of persons who had been acquitted on grounds of
insanity had been established. Until that date the 'prevention of

danger to the community' could not be ensured, as criminal courts had not been vested with legal authority to attach any conditions to the liberation of a person who had been found *non compos mentis*. The more comprehensive regulation came however into force in 1851. The Criminal Lunatics Act gave authorities other than those who had passed the original verdict, the power to keep a criminal lunatic confined. Thus a person who had been tried by, say, the Bengal court and was subsequently transferred to Bombay, could be kept in detention. The act also guaranteed that criminal lunatics of European descent would not accumulate in institutions in India, but would instead be sent to England. There they were received into jails (and from 1863 into the State Criminal Asylum at Broadmoor) rather than Pembroke House, where the Company's lunatics would under ordinary circumstances be accommodated.[67]

The consequences of the Criminal Lunatics Acts were not only of a long-term medico-legal, but also of a short-term practical nature. By the 1840s the European asylums in the three main centres were sufficiently overcrowded to make any increase in admission rates (as was to be expected as a direct result of the new legislation) the last straw that would threaten the institutions' capacity to cope. As no funds for the extension of asylum provision had been allocated by the provincial governments, a more restrictive admission policy appeared to be the only way of dealing with the growth in patient numbers. The problem was most pressing in Bombay and Madras where, unlike in Calcutta, Europeans and Eurasians were admitted alongside Indians. The question was who among the insane should in future be excluded? If criminal lunatics had by force of the law to be admitted, it was other inmates who had to go. Priorities had to be set, and the obvious choice was to prevent local authorities from certifying those among the Indian insane who were considered 'harmless' or merely 'idiotic'.

The basic criteria for the admission of Indians was to become their danger to the community at large rather than their state of mind. The criminal lunacy laws therefore did much to bring out into the open one major aspect inherent in lunacy policy towards Indians, namely its double function as a means of guaranteeing public peace and order, and of controlling and disciplining socially harmful misfits. The oft-proclaimed humanitarian ambition of governments in India to provide a refuge or retreat for those amongst its subjects who were afflicted by insanity and idiocy (regardless of whether they be violent) had fallen prey to the necessities of cost-effective institutional management and considerations for the safety of the expatriate community alone. Dr J. Macpherson, temporarily in charge of the Calcutta Asylum, could thus pointedly summarize the Indian governments' lunacy policy by contrasting the situation in England where 'we provide for our poor, for our sick, and for our insane' with that in India where 'we exhibit an utter disregard of all except criminal lunatics'.[68]

In the case of European lunatics the situation was again evaluated differently from that of Indians. Both the violent and the harmless amongst them were to be regarded as fit subjects for institutionalization and subsequent transfer to England. This does not however imply that the authorities were guided only by the ambition to provide, if not for Indians, at least for Europeans 'for the reception and treatment on the most approved system' (although officials such as governor Falkland may genuinely have interpreted their office to be that of an agent for humanitarian measures).[69] Nor could the tendency amongst the British to 'cling together' and to support their fellow expatriates on patriotic grounds sufficiently account for the preferential confinement of Europeans of all sorts. Patriotism and a sense of togetherness could after all easily be undermined by observance of rules of social precedence, feelings of social superiority, and the omnipresent Victorian aspiration to show kindness only to those who were seen to be 'deserving'. A large proportion of the insane were in fact lower-class soldiers. (In 1850, the Bengal Asylum for example confined fifty-five patients of 'European habits', of whom thirty-three or 60 per cent were in the second class. In Bombay, in 1851/52, twelve out of a total of fifteen Europeans belonged to the lower classes, with all but one, a female pauper, having previously served in the army and navy.[70]) Many of these had, as the Victorians would have put it, indulged in vice and alcohol, had not been able to control their willpower, and could consequently not easily be categorized as belonging to the 'deserving poor'.

If humanitarian and patriotic grounds alone could not easily account for the policy of attaching no conditions to Europeans' admission to the asylum, and in particular for the neglect of the (at other times) so prevalent factors of social background and previous life-habits, what then were the reasons behind it? To a large extent it was of course a result of the authorities' less benign endeavour to leave no white person at large whose behaviour could endanger public safety or military discipline, or which could be considered to adversely affect the prestige of the European community by exhibiting uncontrollably irrational or indecent behaviour unbecoming to a ruling elite. Moreover, in the face of overcrowded institutions and financial prudence, European lunatics could in general not easily have been made the prime target for admission restrictions and cost-cutting exercises. Compared with the steadily growing number of institutionalized Eurasian and Indian lunatics, the number of Europeans in institutions in India was negligible. This was of course largely due to the established practice of sending them back to Europe at regular intervals – towards the middle of the century as often as twice a year. European lunacy consequently became less and less visible both within and without institutions in India. The European mentally ill could therefore not possibly be perceived to be the cause of crowding in institutions in India, and even had the Company been alarmed by the high cost of repatriating Europeans certified insane, they would hardly have been willing to revert to a policy which would have made European lunatics objects for public comment because of their visible presence in the community.

It appears then that the consolidation of lunacy policy in the three provinces and the ultimate legal provisions for British India's European mentally ill had been effected towards the end of the Company's administration of East Indian affairs – despite sometimes conflicting ideological aspirations. Measures were executed by a local administration not always free from corruption, and always with one eye on public opinion in both England and India as to the appropriate treatment of the sick, the poor, and the mad in a colonial context which demanded racial and social segregation, economy of public expenditure and the separation of violent lunatics from the socially harmless insane.

2

The institutions

The role of institutionalization

When, in 1858, the Crown took over the political administration of British India, it was also to take charge of public institutions previously established by the East India Company. The Company's legacy of jails, penitentiaries, hospitals, and dispensaries (and to a lesser extent of orphanages, workhouses and schools) was impressive. There existed also several lunatic asylums. The provinces of Bengal, Bombay, and Madras each boasted an asylum for the reception of Europeans, whilst nearly every district had its own 'native lunatic asylum'. Further institutions for the mentally ill had been established in more recently annexed areas, such as Burma, the Punjab, and Sind, as well as in the coastal centre of Sri Lanka, and in such remote territorial acquisitions as Penang and Singapore. In addition to these specialized receptacles, lunatics 'up-country' in inaccessible and desolate areas could be locked up for shorter periods in the more ubiquitous local jails and in cells adjoining dispensaries and regimental hospitals. The British Empire of the mid-nineteenth century was thus, it would appear, well provided with institutions for the confinement of deranged Europeans and Asians.

The Company's provision for European lunatics extended back into the colonial motherland itself. In England, Pembroke House, a privately managed madhouse, specialized in the treatment of insane Europeans sent home from India by the East India Company. This was not the only institution in England for returned lunatics. Distinguished places such as Ticehurst Asylum also received many a mad officer and

Figure 4 Map of Calcutta, showing the Lunatic Asylum, 1842. (Reproduced by permission of the India Office Library and Records and the British Library, London.)

gentleman or lady whose fortunes allowed for confinement in style, whilst Haslar and Great Yarmouth Hospitals as well as Chatham Asylum made provision for the average brand of insane military and naval servant who had (as in the case of royal army servants for example) not been deemed eligible for maintenance in Pembroke House at the East India Company's expense. At the bottom end of the social scale, guardians of the poor in sea ports where East Indiamen put ashore, reluctantly made provision in public asylums or workhouses for pauper lunatics found wandering at large subsequent to their arrival from India, or who had had an eventual relapse after temporary spontaneous recovery on board ship.

Provision for the mentally ill on such an organized scale may legitimately be regarded as an institutional 'network'. The web of Victorian institutionalism, it would appear, closed in on mad Europeans and colonial subjects in the East alike – from Lahore to Colombo and from Madras to the Straits and back to London. However, the numbers involved were small – still nowhere near those characteristic of 'the great confinement' of western Europe, and of France in particular. The European lunatic asylum in Calcutta, for example, contained in the late 1850s around 100 Europeans, whilst the asylums in Bombay and Madras provided on average for not more than ten Europeans each.[1] The small number of European patients is of course partly a result of the Company's policy of repatriating its insane at least once a year. However, Pembroke House, the major institution for the confinement of 'Indian Insanes' – as returned mental patients of European parentage were called in England – did not see an extraordinary number of patients pass through its premises either. From its opening in 1818 until the changeover to the Crown in 1858 about 500 lunatics with previous Indian experience had been on this institution's books.[2] Even if one would allow for roughly as many mental patients again ending up (rightly or wrongly) in one of England's military, pauper, or private asylums, and for deaths during the arduous and lengthy sea journey round the Cape of Good Hope, the total number of Europeans certified 'mad' and confined in a mental institution of one kind or another on arrival from India was not particularly remarkable.

A similar picture prevailed in regard to non-European asylum inmates in British India. Although the absolute numbers involved here may sound more substantial (with the seven 'native lunatic asylums' in Bengal and the North-Western Provinces for example confining in 1854 between 52 and 189 patients, bringing the total to a little over 1,000) they were by no means proportional to these provinces' overall population figures.[3] Despite further provision for lunatics in small stations' jails, only a 'small proportion' of the Indian mentally ill were institutionalized – as had been revealed during the extended investigation into the state of 'native lunatic asylums' from 1852 to 1854.

Institutional statistics of course are never indicative of the actual incidence of 'mental illness' – even if there was no problem in defining what precisely was to be understood by such a complicated social construct. (Nor, for that matter, do numbers by themselves reveal the relevance attributed to the institutional treatment of the insane.) However, institutional statistics, if contrasted with the estimated number of persons at large considered mentally ill, can reveal the frequency with which recourse is taken by the state to the institutionalization of a certain proportion of its insane.

In the case of British India any attempt to arrive at even an approximate assessment of the number of the mentally ill (inside and outside various institutional settings) is however fraught with particular problems. Take again the case of the Indian insane. Government officials as well as medical practitioners considered the number of confined lunatics to be but a small fraction of the total. Surgeon J. Macpherson was even led to assert with sarcasm in 1854 that

> in India . . . we rejoice to say, that we have no complaint to make of institutions mismanaged, that we have no heart-rending records to shew of cruelty towards the insane, or of any of those abuses which formerly gave rise to the deepest indignation in England,

as there existed what he considered to be but scant institutional provision for the confinement of India's mentally ill.[4] 'Our grievances here assume quite another shape', Macpherson went on, 'we have in India to lament the almost entire absence of Asylums of any sort of description'. In similar vein governor Falkland had in 1850 lamented the insufficiency of public provision for those amongst the insane in Bombay who were harmless, though (in the governor's judgement) still entitled to 'sympathy and assistance from (their) fellow men'.[5] There had also been frequent complaints by European citizens, greatly stirred by reports of madmen allegedly waylaying nervous gentlemen in dark and spooky hollows, pointing up that the Company had as yet failed to securely lock up many a potentially threatening lunatic.

Although government officials, medical practitioners, and European citizens agreed that institutional provision for Indian lunatics was inadequate, their concerted lamentation was apparently insufficient to induce the Company to allocate more funds for the amelioration of the situation. However, more importantly in this context, although the numerical insufficiency of asylums had been condemned, nobody could as yet provide exact data on the relative incidence of madness amongst Indians, nor could anybody estimate with even a moderate degree of reliability the number of lunatics at large. Attempts at estimates were hopelessly contradictory, being based mainly on guesswork and speculation. The superintendent of police in Bombay, for example, who was in 1849 entrusted with establishing reliable population figures, admitted failure.[6] Even census officials in the 1870s pointed out that in the case of lunatics and idiots information was most difficult to obtain because of families' tendency to hide deranged relatives from public sight on the one hand, and the enumerators' lack of diagnostic skill on the other. Data on the number of the mentally ill (and indeed to a certain extent also on the population as a whole) could not, it was suggested, 'be accepted as of much value'.[7]

The situation was no better in regard to European lunatics. Here institutional provision had never been considered to be inadequate. On the contrary, space was always available for European lunatics in any one of the three main receptacles – if only because Eurasian and Indian patients were made to vacate rooms and squeeze into overcrowded wards in Bombay, or because Europeans of higher social standing would be boarded out to more 'suitable' premises in Madras towards the middle of the century, when the building had become dilapidated. Nevertheless, the incidence of mental illness amongst Europeans cannot be simply deduced from the asylums' statistics. To begin with, it was difficult to delineate mental illness from physical disease and from social delinquency. After all, it was a fairly arbitrary decision whether a debilitated, perhaps violent or indecent, hungry vagrant, suffering from some disease, was a fit subject for reception – if at all – into the madhouse, the jail, the hospital, the sailor's home, or the house of correction. The line between disease, crime, insanity, and poverty could not be clearly drawn.

Then, there exists no way to establish the frequency with which mentally deranged Europeans were dealt with by means other than confinement in one of the provincial mental hospitals. Apart from the asylums in Calcutta, Madras, and Bombay, private lunatic asylums received Europeans of a 'respectable class', and civil surgeons made separate provision for private patients. Yet no data are available that could indicate the frequency with which recourse was had to facilities in the private sector. Further, a number of insane civilians simply remained in the care of their friends and relations, as the Bengal medical board pointed out in 1851: 'from natural affection and also from disinclination to lodge their relatives in a public Mad House, however well conducted, the patients are retained by their families'.[8]

Moreover, unruly and strange behaviour exhibited by personnel in the naval and military services was met in the first instance by disciplinary action such as incarceration, flogging and physical training rather than specialized medical care, so that only the most serious cases of mental derangement would appear as such in regimental statistics. Casualty and suicide rates, too, were largely affected by mental problems – yet such connections would not usually be detected from the statistics. And last but not least, only a small number of those diagnosed by the military authorities as insane were finally despatched with the invalids of the season from military camps in the interior to the asylums in the provincial capitals.[9] Junior and senior officers were often sent straight to the nearest port of embarkation for transfer back home to England, as is evidenced by the example of a Lieutenant R. Bruce who had been diagnosed 'intellectually insane', and kept under observation at the 1st Grenadiers' camp for about three months before he was deported without ever being admitted to a lunatic asylum in India.[10] Soldiers and sailors, too, would (contrary to the officially prescribed procedure) not always be received into the asylum. Surgeon Macpherson noted in 1854 that

> about one European soldier has annually passed through
> the [Calcutta] Asylum, and probably nine more may have

59

gone home with the invalids, not being considered bad enough cases to be sent to the Asylum, or may have been sent with invalids, via Bombay, or may have died in the acute stage.[11]

Macpherson based the estimate on his experience as army surgeon and asylum superintendent, and finally arrived, on the basis of his own calculations, at a number 'absolutely sent away from their Regiments for insanity' of 8.5 per thousand (for the period 1848 to 1851), whilst stating that 'the number of admissions into Hospital for insanity among European Troops in Bengal for the four years ending with 1851–52 has been 2.7 per thousand'.[12] Other sources, too, indicate that the incidence of lunacy amongst Europeans may have been a multiple of what official asylum figures lead one to believe. Regimental statistics drawn up for the commission on the state of the health of the army in India reveal that in the Bengal Infantry, for example, 97 per cent of those affected with mental derangement during the period 1847 to 1851 were reported to have returned to duty again. Personnel suffering from insanity had been admitted to the regimental hospital without ever being transferred to the province's only institution specializing in the treatment of mental illness – and would consequently not appear in asylum statistics.[13]

Two points of importance emerge from reflection on the statistics of institutionalization. First, the lunatic asylum was of but minor numerical significance compared with both confinement in less specialized institutions such as hospitals and jails, and informal, disciplinary, or private methods of dealing with unruly and unreasonable behaviour. Second, available statistics consequently provide evidence only for inner-institutional trends and the demographic characteristics of inmates: for fluctuations in admission numbers and mortality rates, patients' professional background, and the diagnoses made, the comparative numbers of first- and of second-class patients, of males and females, and the diet and medical intervention prescribed for different groups amongst the insane. No generalized statement about the incidence of mental illness amongst Europeans in India can be deduced from these data, nor could the socio-political and symbolic relevance of mental institutions within the context of British colonial rule be assessed on the basis of asylum statistics and institutional policy alone. If we want to know more about why, initially, only moderate recourse was taken to confinement in specialized institutions, and what the role of the lunatic asylum within the fabric of British colonial rule was considered to be, we will have to turn to evidence other than that produced in the institutions themselves.

The arguments employed by government officials in favour of the establishment of new asylums in various provinces under British rule are particularly revealing. The official reasoning was in all cases the same. The establishment of 'native lunatic asylums' in Bengal had in 1806, for example, been sanctioned even by the Company's ever cost-conscious court of directors – despite an earlier explicit decree that no large outlay of public funds would be allowed 'at a time when the Finances of the Company experience[d] the pressure of one very expensive War recently concluded, and another lately commenced'.[14] The asylums, the Court duly proclaimed, had 'undoubtedly' for their objects 'the protection of the Public on the one hand, and the relief of the most unhappy Class of human beings on the other'. Despite financial stringency, humanitarian considerations as well as those of public peace and order made the Court therefore 'by no means disposed either to pronounce any harsh or rigid strictures'.

The asylum for Europeans in Calcutta, too, had in 1802 been approved on a similar understanding. The erection of the Madras Lunatic Asylum in 1793/4 had been sanctioned by the authorities in England and India on account of the great advantage that was anticipated to accrue to the town population and to future patients. The hospital board in particular had recommended the asylum project, pointing out 'how beneficial the adoption of it would be to the Community at large by affording Security against the perpetration of those Acts of Violence which had been so frequently Committed by unrestrained Lunatics'.[15]

The cost of such benevolent control lay heavily on the Company's revenue, and despite authorities' endeavours to economize on public services in other areas, local councils seemed prepared to disburse significant sums for its peace of mind and that of its citizens. The rent paid over a fifty-year period by the Madras government, for example, had been an exorbitant three and a half *lakh* of rupees (350,000), and the rate of maintenance in the lunatic asylum had been double that of the general hospital.[16] In other provinces than Madras, too, asylum provision cost the Company many times what it took to maintain institutions of comparable standard in England. Even maintenance costs in hospitals, and more so, in jails, were far below those of madhouses.

Madhouse-owners undoubtedly overcharged the provincial governments. They kept as many inmates as possible at first-class rates, on which the profit margin was wider. Particularly in Bengal during the earlier decade of the century, rates had been charged which (in the words of the medical board in 1847) were

> on a scale of liberality to all connected with the Institution which those accustomed to the more exact and healthier administration of the Public resources of the present day can scarcely contemplate without astonishment'.[17]

For example a Miss Fitzpatrick, who had as an 'out door ward of Kidderpoor school' previously earned Rs 35 per month, whilst in the asylum was maintained on the rate of Rs 100 per month, making available to her 'the enjoyment of a degree of ease and luxury, that [she] never could have expected to procure for [herself] in health', and which, it was speculated by the medical board, must for her as much as for many others with her 'at first have been irksome . . . from its very novelty'.[18]

The fact that many of the patients who benefited from such 'extravagance', were of mixed race, had by the middle of the century undoubtedly become highly objectionable.[19] However, for poor Europeans and lower-class military personnel, treatment on a preferential scale was seen to be no less 'irksome', and the maintenance rate for them was finally also curtailed. Despite cuts in rates, the Calcutta asylum (which had been in the hands of the Beardsmore family for nearly four decades) was even in 1850 still likened to 'Spence's', the town's luxury hotel: the Beardsmores' charges, the accountant general pondered, 'are the same as Spence's; but there it's to be feared the comparison ends'.[20]

To do some justice to the Beardsmores and other asylum proprietors, it must be conceded that the high cost of asylum provision was only partly caused by their tendency to overcharge government. Even subsequent to Lord Dalhousie's reorganization in the 1850s of the medical service and of the lunatic asylum sector, the expense on account of the European insane was to be considerably above average costs in England.

House prices in the three main provinces were notoriously high, and construction and re-construction of asylum buildings was not less costly. Then there was the relatively higher cost involved in keeping inmates of 'European habits' in accordance with the comfort and standard to which they had been accustomed and to which they were considered to be obliged to live up in the colony. In addition to nurses or 'keepers', personal servants were employed to cater for patients' special whims, and some additional European staff had to be available in case a patient needed to be put under restraint and would have felt humiliated to be kept down by a 'native' keeper. Such special personnel requirements made heavy demands on the asylums' already hard-pressed finances.

Nevertheless, the Company seemed reluctant to do without the particular convenience which a madhouse was seen to constitute. What was it then that made this costly institution that catered for but a small proportion of the insane so desirable? The preservation of public peace and order was certainly a main object of concern to Company officials. However, despite the urgency that seems to be conveyed in the official statements, the number of institutionalized lunatics at the turn of the century, when most of the institutions in India had been initiated, was even lower than towards the middle of the nineteenth century. The asylum in Bengal confined in 1818 only thirty European and Eurasian patients who, it might well be argued, could not *in toto* possibly have constituted any insuperable threat to citizens' peace in a place as bustling and unruly as Calcutta. Similarly, Bombay had (in around 1800) only three, and Madras (in 1808) twenty-one Europeans locked up – numbers which make the talk of the places' 'absolute necessity' appear somewhat exaggerated.

Just as the maintenance of public peace and order cannot entirely justify the expenditure on asylums in India, neither can humanitarian motives alone. It may well be admitted that according to contemporary reformist ideology, humanitarian considerations and altruism were believed to be not altogether incompatible with individual self-interest and the Company's wish to control, regulate, and even subjugate people who were considered to exhibit socially undesirable behaviour. Yet humanitarian considerations, too, had their limits as is, for example, evidenced by the decision in the late 1840s to exclude the mentally disabled from institutionalization on account of the relative unobtrusiveness and social harmlessness of their symptoms. Had humanitarian considerations been the main impetus behind the upkeep of highly expensive institutions, then the local governments would indeed not, as governor Falkland succinctly pointed out in 1849, have considered 'to debar a friendless lunatic from all professional aid merely because he may be quite inoffensive'.[21]

The European lunatic asylum in British India possessed a more complex role – one that went beyond the hackneyed rhetoric of peace and order and humanitarian aspiration. The madhouse was, along with other public institutions such as the hospital and jail, one of the symbolic markers of European superiority.

When, for example, Lord Auckland in his capacity as governor-general toured the Upper Provinces from 1837 to 1840, he never missed the opportunity to visit the commercial, police, and medical establishments of even the smallest of British stations. On 28 November 1837 he travelled to Mirzapur and after being greeted by 'the usual assortment of magistrates, judges, collectors, &c. &c.' he immediately 'went off' to see the jail and the famous local carpet manufactories.[22] A week later, in Allahabad, he went to the 'native schools and jails'. In Kanpur, a couple of weeks later, he and 'the gentlemen' of his entourage 'went to the prison to see some Thugs', and again, in camp near Moradabad, a 'cheerful-looking station' (though one where his Excellency's sister was not able to 'find anything to sketch'), he was in the position to pass some time by visiting the local jail after the 'durbar' put on for local officials.

Manufactories, schools, dispensaries, hospitals, court rooms, and jails were some of the showpieces of western colonialism at work in India – brick-and-mortar manifestations of British patriotic pride and self-satisfaction, and intended to be awe-inspiring to the indigenous population. According to contemporary understanding the very existence of institutions was one of *the* proofs of moral and social progress and of the superb character of western civilization and rationality. There could be no better way of expressing this than by maintaining establishments even for those who were devoid of that power of rationality and polite intercourse so highly treasured since the Age of Reason. Insanity itself was in the contemporary mode of expression widely stylized as the 'most grievous malady to which the human family is subject', prompting one medical officer to ask whether there could be 'a more affecting exhibition of suffering than the miserable victim of mental estrangement'.[23] No wonder then, that lunatic asylums would not for long be visited only by high-ranking government officials, but were to become part of travellers' tours of the 'real India', where British stations' first ladies would organize Christmas dinner dances and concerts on the Queen's birthday.

The contemporary view of the European lunatic asylum in India as a showpiece of British humanitarian and scientific progress may strike us as overblown in the light of the small scale and number of actually existing establishments. At the same time it is to a great extent exactly this overstatement, and the disproportionate fervour with which the relevance of the madhouse was advanced, that contributed to the maintenance of the self-image of the British as a superior people whose charitable humanitarianism and rational, scientific achievements made colonial rule appear morally beneficial and legitimate. The legitimacy of colonial rule remained as fiercely asserted as it was disputed, and similarly the institutionalization of the mentally ill remained an important symbolic marker both for enthusiastic advocates and for opponents of an extended British presence in India.

The ideological role of the asylum outlived the Company's administration of East India affairs and persisted up to the heyday of imperial rule, when the confinement of European and Indian lunatics in specialized institutions was implemented on a greater, though still quite modest scale. Then, it appears, asylums were still considered an important enough feature of colonial rule to be made an example of: the liberal member of parliament who (to the consternation of the European community) visited British India in order to convince himself of the propriety of continued British rule in the East, was reported to have asked to be taken 'as a preliminary canter, to the goal and lunatic asylum' where 'he will make many interesting suggestions to the civil surgeon as to the management of these institutions, comparing them unfavourably with those he has visited in other stations'.[24] Afterwards, it was held, he 'will probably write his article for the *Twentieth Century*, entitled "Is India worth keeping?" '.

The European madhouse had, of course, not only positive socio-political and symbolic connotations for the expatriate community. Just as the Georgian and Victorian public in Britain were ambivalent towards public institutions and their clientele, so European town dwellers in India were, to provide just one example, not particularly eager to accept asylums in close proximity to private residencies. In 1851 citizens of Madras managed to divert the local government's plan to considerably enlarge the then dilapidated buildings. They pleaded that government reconsider the purchase of the property in Kilpauk.[25] An enlarged asylum would not only create a nuisance – even 'great injury' – but also declining property prices in the vicinity. Further, the area was judged to be unsuitable as a retreat for the insane: Kilpauk was described as a bustling suburb with the asylum being located close to noisy Indian dwellings, markets, and temples. Similarly, when various plans for the new premises of the Bombay asylum were mooted by government in 1853, locations had to be found which would be neither 'near to nuisances such as noisy trades, or offensive manufactures', nor be likely to become 'surrounded or overlook[ed] or be liable to be inconvenienced by the neighbourhood of public roads or foot paths'.[26]

Generally preferred locations for asylums were isolated areas, ideally as separate from the main hub of colonial town life as the island of Salzette in Bombay. However, the intention of guaranteeing security for the European and Indian public alike, and the early nineteenth-century ideal of the asylum as a 'retreat' cannot entirely account for Europeans' tendency to seek isolated spots for their asylums. The fame of the York Retreat in England (which was situated in pleasing countryside, and for a few decades epitomized the last in asylum construction and enlightened care for the mentally ill) had reached the awareness of reform-conscious government, medical officials, and members of the public in the East, leaving its stamp at least on their rhetoric. Yet, lacking geographically secluded spots in the immediate and easily accessible vicinity of towns, it was in suburbs with primarily Indian populations and lower property prices, like Bhowanipur in Calcutta, where asylums were to be found. Lahore's old lunatic asylum, established by a Dr Honigberger, state physician to Maharaja Dhalip Singh in the early nineteenth century, was situated 'in the heart of the city'.[27] Following the annexation of the Punjab in 1849, the 'unsuitability of the situation' was criticized by the civil surgeon, and consequently new premises were provided. It was considered 'a serious inconvenience to have [lunatics] confined in the middle of the civil station', and they were finally moved to a house that was 'outflanked' by the railway station and 'at a considerable distance from any dwelling-house'. As in many other stations, public institutions such as jails, hospitals, and lunatic asylums were increasingly, if not separated from the European quarters by the railway, then at least placed on the margins of the European parts of town.

Seclusion and isolation thus implied not merely the separation of the mad from those who considered themselves sane. Rather, they came to mean more specifically the separation of the mad from the *European* public. The desire to maintain social distance between those Europeans who thought they were in possession of their wits and those who were considered to have gone 'doolally', was just as strong as the desire to keep people of different social class and racial background apart. Yet the fear of the mentally ill and the wish to keep them well away from European public life were not at all prejudicial to the prevalent tendency to look upon institutions for the mad with pride and satisfaction rather than dismay and embarrassment. The lunatic asylum, inconvenient and threatening as its solid presence in close proximity to European quarters may have been, was after all also a relatively secure and impressive means of keeping the mad at bay. Like schools, orphanages, workhouses and the various sorts of hospitals (the 'general' hospitals for the better-off, the police hospitals for down and outs, the lock-hospitals for the vice-ridden), asylums for Europeans and Indians, too, had become vital elements of the way in which the *pax britannica* was made to assert itself in the East. Surgeon J. Macpherson expressed this when he exclaimed in the 1850s: 'we have our jails, our schools, and our dispensaries in almost every Zillah, and why should we not have our asylums too?'[28]

Towards uniformity

Macpherson's rhetorical question also encapsulates the general feeling amongst most members of the European community: that the best place to keep the mentally ill was behind the walls of British institutions. By the late 1850s nearly every largish *zila* or district would indeed make provision, if not for the European then at least for the Indian insane on a hitherto unprecedented scale. It was, however, not only the scale of measures, but their emergent uniformity and the extent to which institutionalization had become a matter of clearly circumscribed routine, that had changed since the beginning of the century. In that respect the development of the British Indian madhouse followed the pattern characteristic of the situation in the colonial motherland itself, with organized lunacy provision slowly emerging towards the second half of the nineteenth century from a patchwork of highly diverse, and at times controversial, measures.

The visual representation of the European asylum, not least, was to undergo a slow change towards homogeneity. Within half a century institutions as different in external appearance as the Calcutta Asylum (resembling functional city offices), the Madras Asylum (less opulent and during its more advanced years downright shabby-looking in its simple and low-quality army barrack style), and the Bombay Asylum (well-secluded, functional, and horseshoe-shaped) would be replaced by or at least adapted to a modified version of the standard style recommended by the commissioners in lunacy in England. Madhouses in British India were however not a mere replica of institutions in Europe. Nor were they as isomorphous as the mass of buildings constructed by architects and engineers of the reputed public works department. Concessions had to be made to local climatic factors, and, what is more, the quality and comfort of premises varied considerably according to prospective inmates' race and social class.

Further, although medical and government authorities in India were aware of the necessity to adapt European institutional designs to what they called the 'peculiarities' of the climate, and to provide appropriate means of separating various groups among the insane, there would not for a long time yet prevail unanimity about anything even approximating a standard model lunatic asylum. Despite the Company's endeavour to achieve homogeneity in institutional design, mental institutions in British India were only slowly – albeit steadily – moving towards Victorian uniformity. The author of *Hospitals and Asylums of the World* could therefore as late as 1902 maintain that lunatic asylums in India were mainly of the 'irregular or conglomerate type'.[29] In the first and second half of the nineteenth century the diversity was even greater.

The formal status of institutions underwent a similarly slow and not always coordinated, yet steady move towards standardization. Around 1800 all the main European lunatic asylums (Madras, Bombay, and Calcutta) were privately owned by medical officers and were run by them as lucrative income sources. In Bombay a surgeon R. Fildes kept mentally ill European and Indian civilians and military personnel in his private house on the island of Kolaba, to where they had recently been moved from a small institution on Butcher's Island. Assistant surgeon Valentine Conolly received the Madras government's insane employees into his private madhouse in Kilpauk. And in Calcutta assistant surgeon W. Dick owned Bengal's then only private lunatic asylum for Europeans, and had from 1787 offered his medical services and the lease of his establishment to government.

By the 1830s only the Calcutta asylum was still managed by the asylum proprietor, and its then-owner was even (despite the medical board's explicit objections) to be strengthened in his position as a private entrepreneur by the governor-general. In Bombay and Madras, in contrast, government and medical officials had in 1826 and 1808, respectively, virtually abolished the private 'mad-business', and decided to have a medical officer who had no financial interest in the running of the institution take charge of the asylum's management. In addition the authority and controlling role of the medical board was strengthened in these provinces with a view to thwarting corruption and abuse of inmates. By the mid-1850s, however, even the Calcutta asylum had fallen prey to 'nationalization', and from that time onwards the lunatic asylums for Europeans were to be as one in formal status and management structures.

The retention of a private madhouse for the Company's insane in Calcutta must certainly be judged as anomalous. Yet whether an asylum was privately or publicly owned did not by itself determine conditions inside the institution, nor did it guarantee its cost efficiency. The quality of provision and the state of the buildings indeed appear to have been superior in Calcutta where the asylum was privately run by the Beardsmore family from 1821 to 1856. The Bombay asylum, in contrast, built from public funds in the 1820s, and maintained and controlled by government, was, twenty-four years after its inauguration, described by its medical superintendent not only as 'utterly inadequate' but such as to create conditions which made it 'little short of a miracle that a man ever leaves this hospital cured'.[30] Sanitation had become problematic, with the drainage and cess-pool system underneath the 'native male wards' resembling 'an augean stable of impurity which it would take the efforts of a Hercules to correct or cleanse'.[31]

Overcrowding posed insuperable difficulties: in 1850, for example, eighty Indian men had to 'be huddled together into a range of apartments originally built and still adapted for the accommodation of not more than 24'.[32] European patients were, however, not affected by overcrowding, as the men (of whom there were but two in 1850) had been allocated one whole ward, which they only had to share with one Eurasian, or 'Indo-Briton', and one 'Portuguese' patient.[33] Neither did the seventeen female patients suffer from want of space on a ward adapted for the accommodation of twenty-four.[34] Yet their curative treatment was adversely affected since the asylum's doctor had to spend a considerable proportion of his time in attempts to establish order and discipline on the wards where 'dangerous characters' were 'cooped up' with 'quiet and harmless' inmates.

The situation was even worse in the Madras asylum. Here the building had become structurally unsound by the 1840s – only fifty years after it had been constructed as a private enterprise by Conolly. The superintending surgeon described the place in 1846 as being in a 'highly dangerous state',[35] having originally been built of material of the most inferior quality, and 'extremely ill calculated in every way for a Lunatic Asylum'.[36] 'Many of the Cells', he maintained, 'are so inferior in every particular that in England criminals of the worst description would not be confined in them'.[37] Unlike the Beardsmores' asylum in Calcutta, parts of which have survived well into the twentieth century, Conolly's madhouse had already by the middle of the nineteenth century become 'incapable of restoration'.[38]

This fact lay heavily on the Madras authorities, in particular as they had within half a century invested the extraordinarily high sum of three and a half lakh of Rupees (350,000) for the building in rent alone (while the estimated construction cost of the new Madras lunatic asylum that was to be completed in 1871, amounted to a mere one and a half lakh of Rupees). What is more, the local government had originally provided the land on which Conolly's institution was erected, and had paid the salary of the European staff. From 1823 onwards the institution had been 'private' only formally, as the former owner's heirs to whom he had bequeathed the building, engaged an agent to administer the routine affairs of the property and to negotiate with government.[39] Nevertheless, no major improvements in the building's state were undertaken, the supreme government in Bengal declined the local authorities' wish to erect badly needed new premises, and the place that had once been a flourishing and profitable enterprise went into gradual decay so that towards the middle of the century European patients of the higher classes would usually no longer be admitted.

Although asylum reformers in England and India strongly favoured the conveyance of private institutions into public hands on grounds of the anticipated better surveillance of patients' condition and the prevention of suspected abuse, it was of the three main asylums for Europeans the privately owned and managed Calcutta asylum that was to make provision on a comparatively high and relatively constant level. In 1856, it too was taken over by government. From then onwards it was to enjoy the mixed blessing so often typical of public sector establishments, and hitherto shared by the asylums in Madras and Bombay: increased surveillance of accounts and of management practices on the one hand, and deterioration of the quality of provision for patients of the lower classes on the other.

Regardless of the asylums' formal status, patients' life inside the three main asylums depended during the early years greatly on the medical officers' personal styles of management, their motivation for the job at hand, and their professional expertise and approach to treatment. Moreover, the Indian medical service offered ample scope for individuals' initiative (especially prior to its reorganization by autocratic Lord Dalhousie). This could not be more poignantly illustrated than by reference to one of the Bombay medico's devotion to his work. William Campbell, assistant surgeon and asylum superintendent at Kolaba, was not only instrumental in pressing upon government the necessity of enlarged asylum premises but also took great interest in his patients' illness, and even in their former life and personal problems. The case-reports which he sent to Pembroke House in London were outstanding not only in being most elaborate but also in paying implicit tribute to Campbell's empathy with and understanding of patients' woes. Such personal and professional virtues, in Campbell's case verified by his patients' gratitude, was not always the case. As evidenced by flimsy case-descriptions and lack of data on individual inmates, the medical officers in charge of the asylum in Madras were less intensely involved than Campbell in the care of their protégés.

In Calcutta, in contrast, the Beardsmores' humanity and sense of duty had been reported by the medical board to have received favourable comment by the more distinguished among their patients – yet indignation was also expressed at the Beardsmores' lack of an 'intimate' and 'cultivated' knowledge of asylum science.[40] Only a few years previously, however, patients had suffered considerably inferior conditions and uncaring treatment. One of the Beardsmores' predecessors, surgeon J. Sawers, had made provision for the province's lunatics in a place which was described as 'damp, sultry and gloomy'.[41] And if one was to trust Mr I. Beardsmore's evidence, Sawers tended to honour his medical duty in the breach, not turning up when called for emergencies and failing to carry out routine visitations.

Such diversity in asylum conditions and patient–doctor relations in early nineteenth-century India was greatly facilitated by the relative lack of centralized administrative direction and professional regulation and sanction. Yet, diversity and experiments were not always considered to be a bad thing. Eminent government officials such as Elphinstone and Munro argued, rather romantically, the case against a structure of government that they dreaded becoming 'a state of dull uniform repose',[42] and stressed that 'our government should still be considered as in a great measure experimental; and it is an advantage to have three experiments, and to compare them in their progress with each other'.[43] Each of the specific approaches to the treatment of the insane could also more or less convincingly be justified by reference to one or other of the numerous methods that mushroomed in England. The early part of the nineteenth century was after all the time of diverse experiments in the management and the medical and psychological treatment of the insane. No standard technique had as yet emerged, nor was any single theory of madness' causation and cure accepted by the Anglo-Saxon scientific community. What one doctor claimed to have used with success was dismissed disparagingly by the next.

This situation was however to change drastically by the middle of the century. The tendency towards uniformity of asylum management and provision is most succinctly captured by the general attention to detail, evidenced in the asylum rules devised for European lunatic asylums in India in 1856 by surgeon T. Cantor of Calcutta.[44] Cantor was firmly convinced of the need first of all to clearly establish a hierarchical chain of command amongst the staff. He accordingly drew up separate sets of rules for the guidance of the asylum's subordinate officers (usually consisting of a matron, apothecary, steward, and two overseers) and the 'native establishment' (consisting in the case of the eighty-patient Calcutta asylum of about seventy to eighty employees of different status, representing professions as diverse as that of keepers, watchmen, servants, cleaners, and ladies' maids as well as cooks, gardeners, water-carriers, carpenters, and tailors). The hierarchical order was headed by Cantor himself, to whom subordinate officers had to report the general state on the wards and, on occasion of his twice-daily visitation, any emergencies and irregularities. The Indian staff was to communicate with him only through the mediation of the head keeper, who in turn would first call on one of the subordinate officers.

Surgeon Cantor further intended to have the lunatic asylum hermetically sealed from the scrutinizing eye of the public at large. Patients were forbidden to cultivate any contact with people outside the asylum, and subordinates were responsible for submitting any 'communications to or from the patients' to the superintendent.[45] Similarly, servants were explicitly required 'not secretely to carry letters, messages or articles to or from the Patients'. For the first time in the history of the European lunatic asylum in India the flow of information between asylum inmates and the outside world was considerably curtailed. Above all, nobody apart from the superintendent was entitled to respond to 'enquiries concerning the Patients or the Institution'.

The general atmosphere was to become more and more like that described by Goffman as pervading 'total institutions'. The Indian staff was even forbidden to 'talk loudly' and was required to undergo the patronizing ordeal of having to listen to a 'Bengallee translation' of the asylum rules during the monthly muster.[46] The keepers' day and night watch routines were meticulously laid down in that nine of them had to be on duty in the wards from 8 a.m. to 4 p.m. and from 4 p.m. to 8 a.m., respectively. Theirs was mainly a controlling and disciplining duty, as during the night they had to 'go round all the wards every quarter of an hour, to ascertain that the Patients are in their rooms'. During the day they had to 'prevent the Patients from leaving the wards between the hours of out door exercise'. The specific duties of the subordinate officers were less rigidly circumscribed as it was seen to be 'impracticable concisely to define the duties of each individual'. Instead they were 'readily and cheerfully to render their assistance, whenever required'.

Even the hitherto customary practice of having the superintendent reside within the confines of the asylum premises, and thus within easy reach and open sight of patients, was strongly questioned by Cantor on grounds that

> while living absolutely in the midst of the patients, and being thus brought almost hourly into contact with them, his authority and general efficiency become abridged and impaired, his intercourse with them being virtually rather that of a keeper than of a Supervisor.[47]

For the sake of the increased discipline expected to be occasioned by physical distance between superintendent and patients, Cantor was permitted to reside in separate apartments. He vacated his previous quarters for the use of subordinate officers (whose authority and respect was apparently not expected to suffer by close contact with inmates).

Admittedly, reforms other than those directed at reduced transparency of the institution and at tightened discipline among staff and patients had also been effected by Cantor. He emphasized that 'unwearied kindness is under all circumstances to prevail in the treatment of the Patients' and that the 'native Servants, male and female' have to 'abstain from harsh language, threats, abuse, blows and all other acts of oppression or violence'.[48] Professional inspection, too, was guaranteed to a certain extent, as members of the medical board and the chief magistrate were admitted to examine asylum records. However, asylum visitations had, in principle, been part of government officials' duty prior to Cantor, and the requirement to treat asylum inmates with humanity and kindness had been expressed by many superintendents before him. Even Mr I. Beardsmore, who had frequently been criticized by the medical board as an 'industrious but uneducated man', had been familiar with the jargon of the period and had emphasized the necessity of 'moral management', 'non-restraint', and 'humane and kind' treatment.[49] Nor was the talk of discipline and order altogether unheard of before Cantor's time. What, however, made the difference between earlier rhetoric and practice, and Cantor's regime of the 1850s was the care with which the latter was clearly circumscribed and the extent to which it was actually implemented. Cantor acted promptly to realize his reforms. For example, within only four months he brought the expenditure on account of second-class patients down to half by economizing on their diet – an innovation that was according to Cantor met by 'no complaint'.[50]

The change effected by Cantor in the 1850s was on balance one for the worse from the point of view of second-class inmates. The differences become particularly obvious if his asylum rules are contrasted with those that had officially been in force in the three European asylums around 1800. The regulations for the Bengal lunatic hospital that had been drawn up in 1789 for Dick's asylum in Calcutta, for example, consisted mainly of a guideline for proper classification of patients.[51] (Patients were divided into five different classes. For each class the superintendent was allowed to charge a particular rate which was usually commensurable with the patients' former social background. Subaltern officers were worth their former pay and *batta* (special allowances). For sergeants and privates, too, the superintendent was allowed to draw the amount of their pay and *batta*. Persons who had not been affiliated to the Company's service were seen to 'have no particular claim upon Government'. Those in the 'character of Gentlemen' were therefore downgraded from the initially suggested 176 Rupees – the equivalent of a Lieutenant's pay and *batta* – to 100 Rupees. Poor Europeans were in contrast classified like privates. And finally for ladies the money drawn by the superintendent from the Company's accounts amounted to the equivalent of a Lieutenant's pay, namely to around 176 Rs.)

The rules about financial arrangements were supplemented with further guidelines for more general asylum management. The Bombay authorities for example specified that the provision with 'Stocks, Hand-cuffs +ca' was to be guaranteed by the Company, and together with those of Madras they stipulated that 'The Hospital . . . be at all times open to the Inspection of the members of the Medical Board, and to the Civil Magistrate, but to no other Person, without a Ticket from the Surgeon'.[52] Yet, there was no provision made that would *ensure* the regular inspection of the premises. Similarly, the Bengal medical board had in 1821 drawn up more detailed regulations which referred to such essential details as admission and discharge procedures, visitations, medication, patients' clothing, bedding, diet and recreation, and record keeping. The superintendent of the day, Mr I. Beardsmore, however never assented to these. In his outright rejection of official control he was supported by government, and was consequently allowed to pursue his own regime.

With Cantor's appointment as superintendent of the supreme province's only European lunatic asylum the stern spirit of discipline, internal control, regimentation, and financial economy came to pervade this institution's hitherto more open and permissive atmosphere. By the 1860s Cantor's innovations had diffused throughout British India and become part and parcel of nearly all asylum regimes. Daily food rations were then officially prescribed and dished out to the ounce, and patients' segregation and classification were strictly and uniformly enforced. The lunatic asylum had become a place where, as Foucault put it, 'order no longer freely confronted disorder, reason no longer tried to make its own way among all that might evade or seek to destroy it'.[53]

Inside the institutions

Asylum conditions deteriorated towards the middle of the century, though one group among the European insane was but slightly affected by this tendency: higher-class inmates. They had never really been deprived of the facilities and comfort their social position was assumed to demand. They had always been lodged in superior apartments, separate from the (so-to-speak) madding crowd on the wards. Their diet, clothing, and means of recreation were both generous and luxurious. They were waited upon by personal servants or ladies' maids, and – when nearing convalescence – enjoyed some freedom of movement and the attention and occasional polite company of the superintendent. In the Beardsmores' asylum in Calcutta, for example, they frequently dined at the family table. In Bombay surgeon Campbell regularly went for walks at the beach with them, engaging in small-talk and enjoying the superb panorama of the city's harbour with its sailing-ships, and of the hills that could be glimpsed on the horizon. A patients' library (in Calcutta even equipped with a *punkah* or fan), was another amenity made available for the use of first-class inmates. Reading material such as the *Illustrated News*, *The Times*, and *Punch* was on offer, along with amusements such as chess, draughts, backgammon, domino, kaleidoscopes, and in a few instances, music.[54]

Only in Madras were higher-class patients more seriously affected by the decline in institutional conditions. There the building itself had by the middle of the century come so close to dereliction that alternatives to confinement in the asylum had to be taken recourse to. But even then every effort was made to provide conditions for first-class patients as conducive to their physical comfort and peace of mind as possible. Captain John Campbell of Madras, for example, acquitted of a charge of murder on account of his deranged state of mind, had been allocated a whole wing in the jail (the asylum being considered 'unsuited for persons of his class').[55] In order to maintain his comfort and to guarantee his security (not to mention that of those around him), the other inmates were made to squeeze up in the remaining smaller part of the institution, and the staff had to suffer even greater than normal difficulties in maintaining order, occasioned by overcrowded conditions and the presence of an 'unruly madman'.

The deterioration of the buildings for the mentally ill of the Bombay province was not as advanced as of those in Madras. Yet overcrowding was here, too, a problem, and conditions were bad enough to induce the medical board to express their indignation. 'Treatment, whether moral, medical, or hygienic', was considered to be 'surrounded by difficulties, all but unsuperable'.[56] Various projects, expected to ameliorate this situation, such as the transfer of mentally disabled patients to a specially designed 'village of imbeciles', were considered. In 1850 'harmless idiots', the 'fatuous', and 'imbeciles' (as the mentally disabled were called) made up about 55 per cent of the asylum population, so that had they been boarded out, the asylum's overcrowding would have been considerably alleviated.[57] Another option considered was to confine 'criminal lunatics' in separate premises. This, too, would have greatly eased the pressure on the European lunatic asylum, as in consequence of the criminal lunatics acts of 1849 and 1851 the number of this special group among the insane had risen steadily. Yet another alternative canvassed was to allocate a separate institution to 'insane native soldiers', and to fill up any consequent vacancies with 'criminal lunatics'; or to keep the existing institution as a depot for Europeans *en route* to repatriation, and to construct a new asylum for the remaining Indian and Eurasian patients.

Although any of these suggestions would have alleviated the congested conditions in the Bombay asylum, they would have been costly to realize and would consequently have generated controversy. A much more straightforward and cost-saving measure would have been simply to change the system of classification and segregation that was used in the asylum, which by itself actively generated overcrowding. Of the four wards available (each designed to accommodate between twelve and seventeen inmates) two were allocated to 'native males', one to 'females', and another to 'Europeans'.[58] In 1850 seventeen female patients were confined without problem on a ward of their own. The second ward, too, could hardly have been considered congested with only four patients of 'European habits'. The remaining eighty patients (80 per cent of the asylum population, exclusively Indians and lower-class Eurasians) were left with only half the building.

Despite these manifest disparities even the superintendent pointed out that the mere statistics did not convey 'an adequate conception of the real nature and magnitude of the disproportion which actually exists'.[59] He went on to explain that

> of these 80 lunatics there are eight whose symptoms and peculiarities are such as to render it absolutely indispensable that they should each be confined in a separate place so that 16 cells only are left for the accommodation of 72 individuals.

If one takes into account that each of those cells measured only two by three metres, the superintendent's concern that not only Victorian precepts of decency and morality but also the effectiveness of treatment and the security of inmates were at stake, appear well-founded. 'The case is still further aggravated', he wrote in his petition for new asylum premises to government,

> when we consider the total disregard for decency and propriety which those afflicted with insanity so frequently

manifest. Their propensities are often filthy and disgusting in the extreme – they go about naked – they obey the calls of nature wherever they are sitting or laying, and I leave it to the imagination of the reader to depict what must be the state of premises so limited, crowded with human beings, many of whom have habits so revolting – surely this requires no comment.

Such inadequacies made the 'treatment and cure of the most grievous malady to which the human family is subject' difficult, and 'could it', the surgeon asked, 'be wondered at, had I 'ere another day has run its course, to report a murder or a suicide within these walls?'[60]

Bad as conditions in the Bombay lunatic asylum appear to have been, it should be noted that it was mainly the Indian and Eurasian insane who bore the brunt of them – mainly because of officials' dogged insistence on race-, class-, and gender-specific segregation. Even at a time when the medical officer in charge of the institution pressed government to lose no time 'in doing something to ameliorate the condition of the unhappy wretches' on his wards, he himself would, of course, not even contemplate a change in classificatory practice.[61] Even though he had pointed out that 'inmates could theoretically be accommodated without problems, if they were equally distributed over the different parts of the premises, . . . difference of sex, caste, and color, rendered this of course . . . altogether impossible'.[62] European first-class patients certainly suffered some of the inconvenience that necessarily went along with the fact of their apartments' close proximity to wards which were characterized by a critic in the local newspaper as being in an 'abominable' state, resembling 'dungeons'. Apart from this, however, they did not experience much deprivation.

For European second-class patients things were more variable, depending mainly on who was in charge of the institution. Surgeon Campbell, for example, usually showed them respect, kindness, and consideration, although the quality of their provision was in general adapted to what was considered to be their 'former habits and tastes'.[63] Gunner F. Harvey, one of Campbell's patients who had been admitted to the Bombay asylum in 1852 as a 'maniac', believing he was the 'spirit of the immortal Byron', expressed his feeling of 'gratitude for the kindly interest' evinced to him by the superintendent. Further, apparently in awareness of the rules of social precedence and of the social gulf between himself and the medical officer, Harvey pointed out that this interest 'becomes more affecting from the infrequency of the exhibition of such a feeling from a superior towards an inferior'.[64] Some of Campbell's predecessors were less inclined to show 'kindly interest' to patients of the 'lower orders of society'.

In no other asylum had the quality of provision, and thence of life within the institution been more varied, being explicitly dependent on inmates' social standing and racial background, than in that of Calcutta. The metropolis of the supreme province of Bengal – the acclaimed 'city of palaces' – had by the early nineteenth century taken over the role of trend-setter from Madras. In particular in regard to social precedence and class-consciousness, the European community in Calcutta was first to develop and last to give up hardened attitudes bordering on snobbery and bigotry. The general climate of racial and social intolerance inevitably also permeated the lunatic asylums. In one respect, however, the European lunatic asylum in Calcutta had an advantage over the institutions in Madras and Bombay: its superintendents had never had to take any pains to create social distance in order to ensure racial segregation. Rather, the Calcutta asylum from 1821 onwards simply no longer admitted any other than European and higher-class Eurasian patients (except in exceptional circumstances, as in the case of mentally ill Indian princesses). 'Assembling Europeans and Natives in one Establishment' was in the words of the medical board, in 1847, evaluated as a 'crude and incongruous scheme'.[65] A couple of decades earlier, in 1821, the board had similarly strongly objected to the Company's court's suggestion that authorities in India 'dispose of the few cases of Insanity in Europeans' by temporarily keeping them in the 'native lunatic asylum' near Calcutta.[66] The 'propriety of mixing Europeans labouring under mental derangement with natives in the same unfortunate condition' was, the medical board held, 'very questionable'.[67] Racial segregation was consequently sustained inter-institutionally, and separate lunatic asylums for Indians and lower-class Eurasians only were to be found from the beginning of the nineteenth century in the major districts: Benares, Bareilly, Patna, Dacca, and near Calcutta, and, towards the middle of the century, in Delhi.

Although the superintendents in Calcutta escaped the task of separating Indians and Europeans, they were, of course, still careful to make appropriate provision for Europeans and Eurasians of different gender and social backgrounds. By the late 1850s the asylum consisted of 'two divisions': one for male, the other for female patients.[68] In all, sixty-three single rooms were available on the various wards. As the number of patients was by that time on average about eighty, second-class patients had to share a cell. Each of these was provided with a window 'well out of reach' and with 'an iron barred door' – the latter allowed the 'free circulation of Air' and was seen to be 'preferable to the solid doors with inspection plates' then common in asylums in England. One ventilation device without which no reasonably well-to-do European household in India would make do, the man-powered *punkah*, was however absent in patients' rooms. Cells were not 'lofty' enough to allow their installation, explained Surgeon Cantor in 1856. It seems, however, that the cost involved in the maintenance of an establishment of *punkah-wallahs* was not an altogether irrelevant factor, especially when patients were more easily 'supplied with a palm leaf fan' which they could operate themselves and the expense of which was negligible, being only 'one pice a piece'.

The rooms for second-class patients were spartanly furnished. Wooden bed-steads, similar to those used in European barracks and hospitals were provided. The floors were unmatted, so that they could be conveniently cleaned and allow for 'baths being applied whenever required', and the only other chattels were 'bed utensils' in case of an inmate's physical disease or manic fits.[69] Violent or ill second-class patients had to stay in their cells at all times, while for the other inmates the rooms opened on to the adjoining verandah, which was 'screened by venetians and canvas curtains'. Tables were spread there for the meals, and lamps were lighted at night, and the more tractable patients would spend most of the time during the 'heat of the day and in wet weather' on these 'common Verandahs'. Each ward was equipped with one 'easily accessible and ample privy and bathing room with shower Baths'. Only in the case of first-class patients, residing in superior, separate apartments was the fact that they had to share the general toilet and bathing facilities of ward patients regretted.

Although nowhere near to the abysmal conditions in Madras and Bombay, 'want of space and accommodation' was by the

1850s in Calcutta also seen as the main obstacle to patients' classification in accordance with their state of mind.[70] The lack of 'isolated wards for refractory patients' in particular was lamented by the medical officer in charge. 'A single violent patient', he argued, 'is sure to produce a number of imitations and to keep the asylum in an uproar, as long as the paroxysm may last'. The benefit all patients were considered to gain from exercise and walks in the garden was in practice available only to a small number of them, and then only for a short time twice a day. The garden, though 'remarkably well laid out', was 'too limited' in extent, 'particularly considering the number of Patients and the paramount importance of extensive pleasure grounds in all Lunatic Asylums'.

It was however not only constricted space and overcrowding that were perceived as detrimental to both treatment and order. Notorious understaffing was also criticized as a major problem. After all, keepers and servants were not 'less essential than cells' for the control and safety of asylum inmates – and there were some occasions when safety was considered to be endangered by a lack of staff.[71] The intensity of care shown by the staff, too, was not always satisfactory. Complaints centred not only on the 'native servants', in none of whom surgeon Cantor, for example, would 'place confidence'.[72] Subordinate personnel, usually invalid European soldiers or young Eurasians, were frequently criticized for neglect of duty or incompetence. It had been common practice until the middle of the century for staff to be hired 'by the day or week like common labourers', and this fact had, as pointed out by the medical board in 1836, adverse consequences for patients, as 'a sufficiency of Male and Female keepers . . . permanently engaged and taught by experience and appropriate instruction to manage persons suffering under various forms of mental derangement' was seen to be 'indispensable to an Institution worthy of the patronage of Government'.[73]

Further, the peculiarities of the Indian climate and the attributes so characteristic of British expatriates exposed to an alien culture and a colonial situation were seen to necessitate modifications in asylum regimes. Arguments from cultural preference and racial propensity were advanced by medical officers in India against one of the highly lauded aspects of what came in Britain to be called 'moral management': patients' engagement in productive work. 'Remedial employment' was considered to be 'utterly inapplicable in tropical India, where the climate renders farming, gardening and occupation in the Kitchen, laundry or bakehouse impracticable, if not injurious to Europeans'.[74] The detrimental effect of manual labour was one of few peculiarly colonial factors that cut across the lines of social class (though not race). 'To the Majority of the Patients at Bhowanipore, Soldiers, Sailors and Gentlemen' alike, mechanical labour was expected to be 'uncongenial'. In India the employment of European inmates was consequently considered to produce exactly the opposite effect to that in Britain.

Non-Europeans, in contrast, were believed to generally benefit from active work, although in their case, too, stipulated racial and cultural differences were taken into account. Surgeon Cantor had, for example, after 'some five months perseverence' succeeded in 'introducing a system of moral treatment, not by compulsion, but by persuasion and well timed rewards' into the Dhalanda native lunatic asylum, near Calcutta.[75] His patients, 'some 300 of the poorer classes of Bengallees', were made to pluck hemp or coir, to make ropes, swabs, and rugs, to spin wool for blankets, or to work in the kitchens and gardens. In contrast to asylum inmates in South East Asia (where Cantor had previously been on duty), Indian patients were less amenable to such 'moral treatment'. Cantor found the introduction of 'voluntary manual labour' to have been 'a task less easy to accomplish at Dullunda [Dhalanda] than it proved in the Lunatic Asylum at Pinang in 1843', where the patients had been 'Malays, Chinese, Klings, Burmese, Siamese, Cochin-Chinese and Hindostanees'. According to Cantor they 'took Kindlier to a variety of light work than has been found the case with the Bengallees'. Similarly, Eurasian patients were expected to loathe manual work. According to common British stereotype they were 'scribblers', or *crannies*, dedicated to secretarial work, and they therefore 'despised all trades, save that of the desk'. Eurasian inmates in the Calcutta asylum who were seen to 'evince their habitual propensity to scribbling' were therefore supplied with slates in order 'to save paper and walls'.

Leisure activities and manual work were not the only means by which 'moral treatment' could be furthered. A regulated time-table and daily routine was considered not less important – and could without particular modification be introduced into asylums in India. In Calcutta where life inside the asylum had been stringently organized by Cantor from the late 1950s onwards, an uninspiring daily routine prevailed:

> The patients rise at gunfire, and are taken for an hour's walk round the garden. Bath and Toilet over, the superintendent pays his Morning visit. The Breakfast and Dinner hours are at 8 and 2 o'Clock. About half an hour before sunset, after the evening visit, the Patients take exercise in the garden. Tea is served at 7. At 8 or not later than 9 o'Clock, the Patients are in bed. The hours intervening between the meals, are filled up according to the condition and fancy of each Patient, in reading, games, conversation, or sleep. Quiet patients are admitted in the Steward's Office, which is also made to serve as reading room and library.[76]

Considering the long intervals during which inmates were left to themselves, time must have hung heavily on their hands. This was however not altogether uncommon in Europeans' life in India even outside the asylum. Military servants, for example, found that being confined to their barracks most of the day tended to 'get on their nerves', in particular during the hot season when temperatures soared and they had to 'sweat it out'. The soldiers would lie on their *charpoys* or beds in the barrack-rooms, 'many of them naked, under a mosquito net to keep the flies off, and the only thing moving was the *punkah* above them going backwards and forwards, backwards and forwards'.[77] Widespread as such ennui and lack of recreational facilities were known to be, no steps towards an amelioration of the situation were taken, either for the rank and file in the military, or for lower-class lunatics in the provinces' asylums.

The question then arises as to what effect, if any, confinement in one of the three European madhouses had on its inmates' condition?[78] No answer as to the effects of the general workings of the asylum regime on patients' minds and well-being can be easily gleaned from the few case-reports produced within the institutions. Nor do scanty accounts by outsiders such as the reputed asylum reformer Sir A. Halliday, or by the lesser known Dr G.A. Berwick provide more reliable information. One may therefore be tempted to conclude that circumstances were similar to those alluded to by the early eighteenth-century traveller (and interloper) Captain Alexander Hamilton in respect to the hospital in Calcutta. Hamilton mused sardonically:

'The Company has a pretty good Hospital at Calcutta, where many go in to undergo the Penance of Physick but few come out to give account of its Operation'.[79]

One alternative way of approaching the question would be to analyse those data which medical boards and asylum superintendents themselves produced in order to attest to the Company and to the public at large, the institutions' and their medical officers' or owners' ability to effect improvements in patients' condition; namely cure, discharge, and mortality rates.

From the asylums' inception superintendents had been obliged to draw up statistics. For the early decades of the nineteenth century these consist mainly of rolls, providing only basic data such as inmates' name, age, profession, date of admission and discharge. Towards the middle of the century the Victorian craze for numbers made itself felt in British India, and medical officers gradually started to put numerical values on their protégés' condition. This process was, however, not without problems, as unreliable and simply miscalculated figures evidence. Conceptual problems, too, could not easily be solved. The decision when to designate a patient as 'cured', 'relieved', or 'uncured' was based more often on guess-work and wishful thinking than on accurate diagnostics. With these caveats, the statistics provided for asylums in British India frequently compared well with those supplied by public institutions in Britain. For example, the total percentage of people discharged as 'cured' from the European asylum in Bengal from 1824 to 1850 lies at 36 per cent but slightly below the rates then common in madhouses in England and Wales.[80]

More problematic were statistics on the number of 'long-term' patients and 'incurable' cases. In the late 1840s it was revealed that a comparatively large number of inmates in the Calcutta asylum had been there for long periods, some for over twenty years. In December 1847, for example, when the statistics showed a total of forty-three inmates, sixteen lunatics had been confined for more than seven years.[81] In England, too, a similar tendency had emerged towards the late 1840s and 1850s. The gradual crowding of institutions with 'chronic cases' had not only contributed to a more pessimistic view of the possibility of curing insanity, but had also caused the authorities to demand more detailed statistics in order to establish asylums' cure- and cost-effectiveness. The medical authorities in Bengal found it difficult to meet this demand, posing, as it did, the problems of

defining constructs such as 'incurability', which at least notion-
ally implied a well-grounded knowledge of the nature of insanity on the one hand, and of the susceptibility of diverse forms
of mental illness to medical treatment and institutional intervention on the other. Such considerations had not to date
preoccupied the medical professionals', let alone the asylum
proprietors' minds to any great extent. The problem was consequently evaded by stating 'as the nearest approximation to a
calculation that those who have been above two years in the
Asylum may safely be pronounced incurable'.[82]

The data gained on this basis were again very similar to those
for England. In both cases the questionable criterion of 'time
spent inside an institution' as an indicator of 'incurability'
reflects the contemporary belief in the institution as the
appropriate measure for the cure of the temporarily insane, and
in the long-term confinement of 'hopeless' cases. Time spent
within the very institution which was designed for the cure and
confinement of mental illness had become an allegedly
objective criterion for the probability of hopelessness!

Circumstances in British India differed however in one
important aspect from those in England. The majority of
European patients were routinely transferred back to Europe.
The bulk of 'long-term patients' was therefore, in the case of the
Calcutta asylum, for example, made up of Eurasians 'of the
lower and middle classes', namely 'petty tradesmen and
paupers',[83] and in that of the Madras and Bombay asylum, of
Eurasians and Indians. This racial specificity tended to
drastically affect cure and mortality rates. Patients whose
relatives were described by the Bombay asylum superintendent as 'poor, ignorant, and superstitious'[84] reached the asylum
only when 'the time has, in most instances, long passed during
which advantage of any kind could be expected from
appropriate scientific treatment'.[85] Similarly, European military
lunatics would frequently be detained for up to a year in
regimental hospitals, before they were sent to the Calcutta
asylum. Factors such as these induced the medical board of
Bengal to maintain that there existed 'no opportunity in the
majority of instances, for ascertaining the effect of treatment in
the Asylum'.

Nevertheless, data were provided, and despite admission that
these could hardly be compared with statistics on institutions in
England, they were in fact set against them. In most cases the

Indian statistics again did not fare badly. The rate of cure (the percentage of cured cases to admissions) had in the Calcutta asylum, for example, averaged about 21 per cent during the period from 1824 to 1850.[86] From 1824 to 1834 it had risen as high as 30 per cent; during the following ten years it decreased to about 16 per cent, reaching a low of 12 per cent towards the late 1840s. Admittedly, some asylum reformers in England believed that (given adequate institutional care) as many as 60 per cent of the mentally ill could be cured. Yet, to do some justice to the Calcutta asylum, it should be set against metropolitan, county, or military and naval asylums in England and Wales rather than prestigious and (due to their selective admission policy) special institutions such as the York Retreat or Bethlem Hospital. Even the Calcutta asylum's lowest cure-rate of 12 per cent (for the 1840s) bears comparison with a rate of only 11 per cent in English and Welsh military and naval asylums. The average rate for metropolitan and county asylums was 15 per cent and 20 per cent, respectively.[87] Whilst better than the rates in Calcutta, they were of the same order. In 1860 the variation of cure rates among various types of asylums in England and Wales was considerably less, with an average rate of 13 per cent and a steady 11 per cent for naval and military asylums. By that date asylums in Britain, as in British India, had been affected drastically by the accumulation of 'chronic' cases.

Only in regard to mortality rates did asylums in India compare unfavourably with institutions in the British Isles. Not only had the mortality rate in the Bengal asylum, for example, increased steadily, but it had during the earlier decades of the nineteenth century been on average twice as high for second-class patients.[88] By 1850 it had reached an alarming 18 per cent, with less divergence in the rates for first- and second-class patients (15 per cent and 19 per cent, respectively). Such figures were well above the norm for England where 'all large and well conducted asylums together' (such as the York Retreat, Bethlem, St Luke's, and Hanwell) were reported to have had an annual mortality-rate of only 9 to 10 per cent.[89] Whilst these may sound high by today's standards, and the aspirations of early nineteenth-century English asylum reformers, within the contemporary English and the Indian context they were in fact not so alarming. Mortality rates in England during the first half of the century showed a wide variation,[90] and in India public institutions in general were notorious for high death-rates.[91] (In the 'Tirhoot Jail', for example, mortality in 1851 had been as high as between 18 and 20 per cent. In the Delhi Jail the figure was considerably lower, namely around 11 per cent, which was, however, still way above an estimated average rate of about 3 per cent for the town population.[92])

Seen within the context of conditions in other institutions in India as well as of a variety of less specialized English asylums, the madhouses in India, though not at all salubrious places, do not appear to have been anything out of the ordinary – at least not in statistical terms. However, professional aspirations in British India continued to grow, and particularly towards the middle of the century some medical officers' aim was to 'bring the insane out of themselves and into contact with all in nature or art or social arrangements that is pleasurable and pure and good'.[93] Needless to say, such sublime designs were in the case of lower-class and 'native' lunatics hardly likely to be realized by confinement under the conditions and regimes prevailing in Indian institutions.

Notwithstanding a tendency towards uniformity under state regulation, institutional provision for the care and control of the European insane in India was proximately determined by the idiosyncrasies of madhouse keepers and medical superintendents. These in turn, however, were conditioned by the sexual, racial, and class mores of the British colonialists, as well as by adaptations of the views on the insane and their treatment prevalent in the British motherland. Consequently, institutional discipline, segregative control of inmates, financial considerations, and the maintenance of the rulers' image characterized the Company's *pagal-khana* or madhouse. A large number of mentally ill Europeans were apparently dealt with in jails, hospitals, or in the community, whilst fewer passed through the portals of a specialized institution. Nevertheless, lunatic asylums played a significant role in the socio-political infrastructure of the Raj and in its ideological legitimation.

3

The medical profession

The search for fortune and professional recognition

In many pre-modern societies the signification of madness encompassed a wide range of conflicting feelings and psychological projections. The mad could be revered or feared as bearers of preternatural powers, they could be despised as monstrous brutes, and the apparent 'simpletons' among them could be romantically idealized as holy, innocent fools or 'naturals', or be ridiculed as village idiots and subjected to atrocities and mean tricks. Those suffering from a more violent strain of madness or subject to melancholic gloominess tended to be approached with the cautious curiosity that is frequently fuelled by admiration and fear – a mixture that might easily find a cathartic release in abuse and brutality or be converted into naive veneration. These diverse ways of responding to madness could prevail simultaneously, or else one particular attitude may be dominant.

Those who dealt with the mad, treating or caring for them, tended to a certain extent to share the stigma that was bestowed upon their charges. Just like the mad they were subject to quickly changing perceptions oscillating between respect and suspicion. This cautious and at times openly hostile attitude can to a certain extent be accounted for by the fact that madhouse superintendents in the late eighteenth century, for example, would not as a rule possess any formal medical qualification, but rather came in many stripes – not uncommonly including clergymen and 'quacks', as well as the medically qualified. Until the passing of the Lunatics Act of 1845 (which obliged each county in England to build its own public lunatic asylum), most

*Dedicated (by Permission) to the Honorable Committee of Shipping
of the East-India Company.*
Published 1st January 1819, price 15s. in boards,

A NEW EDITION
OF A
REGISTER OF SHIPS

Employed in the Service of the United East-India Company,
from the Year 1760 to the present Period, specifying the Number
of Voyages, Tonnage, Managing Owners, Commanders, Officers,
Surgeons, and Pursers, with every Information relating to the
Maritime Service, and a Reference for others connected with
East-India Commerce.

By the late CHARLES HARDY.
Revised, with considerable Additions, by his Son,
HORATIO C. A. HARDY.

London: Printed for and sold by H. Hardy, Jerusalem Coffee
House, Cornhill; and published by Black, Kingsbury, Parbury,
and Allen, Leadenhall Street.

INSANITY.

PEMBROKE HOUSE, HACKNEY,

For the Reception and Medical Treatment of Insane Persons,
Established and carried on by

DR. GEORGE REES, No. 49, FINSBURY SQUARE,

Member of the Royal College of Physicians, Author of Practical
Observations on Disorders of the Stomach, &c.

AND

PHYSICIAN TO INSANE PERSONS RETURNING FROM INDIA,
Under the Patronage of the
HON. EAST-INDIA COMPANY.

THE high encomium which has been paid to the management of
this Establishment, in the late investigation into the state of Mad
Houses by the House of Commons,* and the distinguished patronage
of the HON. EAST-INDIA COMPANY, render it unnecessary to
say any thing more in its favor. It will be sufficient therefore to add,
that the number is limited, the Patients are select, the advantages
are considerable, and the terms reasonable, and that *three-fourths
of those already admitted have been restored to health and reason.*

Further Particulars may be known by applying either at *Pembroke
House* or in *Finsbury Square,* where Dr. Rees attends on Tuesday,
Thursday, and Saturday Mornings, from Ten to Twelve.

Male and Female Attendants, of approved experience, sent to any
part of the Kingdom.

* *Vide First Annual Report of the Committee of the House of Commons
appointed to examine into the State of Mad Houses, page 17.*

U u 3

Figure 5 Advert on Pembroke House, Hackney, 1819. (Reproduced
by permission of the India Office Library and Records and the
British Library, London)

madhouses were private investments – a fact which did not help to reduce mad-doctors' ambivalent social image and generally low professional repute. It was widely held by both the public and medical professionals such as A. Duncan (professor of medical jurisprudence at Edinburgh), that '[f]ew speculations can be more unpleasant than that of a private mad-house, and it is seldom if ever undertaken, unless with the hope of receiving large returns on the capital advanced'.[1]

In awareness of the charge made by social critics such as Sir A. Halliday (that madhouse owners were 'wholesale dealers and traffickers' in a particular 'species of human misery'[2]) and the suspicion raised by J. Conolly (that 'the prospect of certain profit' attracted the ignorant and uneducated and those who were 'capable of no feeling but a desire for wealth'[3]), mad-doctors with a medical background were keen to accentuate the rational and scientific medical expertise they believed their profession to have acquired with the Enlightenment. By the 1840s the medical profession as a whole had achieved the aim of being – at least in the eyes of the law – acknowledged as the highest faculty, and the sole experts in matters of healing. They had established their own professional associations and laid down regulations for medical training. By the late 1850s they had taken steps against the trading of medical diplomas and degrees, and had begun to publish scientific journals and conference proceedings.

Yet those doctors involved in the superintendence of madhouses would not (despite the formal trappings of professionalization and progressive medicalization) for many decades enjoy the high status accorded to what in the vernacular came to be known as the 'demi-gods in white'. Within the discipline of medicine as a whole, psychiatry occupied a marginal position, and those medical doctors who were involved in the care of the mad were met with but barely concealed suspicion and condescension by their own colleagues. During the second half of the nineteenth century experts in lunacy still had to concede that they specialized 'in a department of science the first principles of which are not recognized by their medical brethren'.[4]

In Britain the rise of the medical profession (and in particular of the mad-doctor) to professional autonomy and expert status had been a slow process, marred by charges of financial embezzlement, inefficiency, and abuse of patients, and protracted by setbacks in legal battles against members of the less well-connected healing arts (such as bone-setters, 'quacks', and women-doctors). The social and professional status of the staff employed as medical officers by the East India Company was even more ambivalent, and the nature of their expertise was the subject of a great deal of controversy. Highly diverse graphic accounts were given of medicos' backgrounds and abilities, which did not fail to capture people's imagination and prejudices. The claim that a 'butcher got a Surgeon's certificate' in 1758[5] is but one pertinent example. Chevers' anecdote, related in 1854, of '[t]he *Philosophic* Surgeon, who on his way to his indigo factory, would enquire of the native doctor – "Any thing to-day" – and, upon receiving the ready answer, "All's well, Lord of the world, only five men dead", would exclaim cheerfully – "good, very good" – and canter gaily about his business', is another.[6]

A good many such stories were certainly highly caricatured, but they contained a grain of truth. After all, up to the late eighteenth century, candidates for the medical services would be nominated by the directors of the East India Company, and until 1800 the Corporation of Surgeons, London, issued what was considered to be an inferior diploma qualifying applicants for appointments as hospital mate or assistant surgeon in an Indian province. Although in 1773 a professorial board had been established in London to examine candidates for the Company's medical service, this did not prevent aspirants from having recourse to less arduous ways of obtaining an appointment in the Orient, as evidenced by an advert in *The Times* of 6 March 1806:

> FIFTY POUNDS may be had by procuring the Advertiser an ASSISTANT SURGEONCY in the East India Company's service. Address (postpaid) to A.M., at Peele's Coffee-House.[7]

What prospective appointees such as 'the Advertiser' were after, was frequently not so much a fulfilling position as a medical officer, but the potentially large fortunes that could be made in the East. The residency surgeoncy at Lucknow for example, was estimated to have brought in in 1785 as much as Rs 8,000 per month – a most tidy sum, largely made up of the allowances by one of the princely houses. Prize money, available to Company's surgeons as they held commissions, were a further income source that could amount to sums as high as Rs 22,478 or Rs 11,239 at the 'battle of Bijaigarh' (for a surgeon or assistant surgeon, respectively).[8] Then medicos could also, like Chevers' 'Philosophic Surgeon', 'frankly and unashamedly indulge in trade':[9] in the highly lucrative manufacture of indigo or other profitable activities.

No other additional income source for high-flying surgeons was however more disapproved of and likely to incite distrust in the sincerity of their professional motives than the exploitation of hospital contracts. Until 1815 (in Bengal, and 1827 and 1828 in Madras and Bombay, respectively) it was usually part of the regimental surgeon's duty to provide food, liquors, bedding, clothing, and certain medicines for patients under his charge. The temptation to economize on articles (to the detriment of the sick) appears to have been one that but few medical officers resisted. In the 1836 edition of the *India Journal of Medical and Physical Science*, for example, the story was related that in 'Lord Lake's camp such were the enormous receipts in consequence of these contracts for supplying corps with medicine, diet, and dhoolees, that Doctors Monroe and Cockrane especially realised the largest fortunes ever made in this country'.[10]

Many more charges of this sort were made – usually not without some overtone of admiration. A Joseph Hume, who had held the title of 'MD' (St Andrews), for example, had come to India in 1797 in search of a fortune and had obtained the position of 'assistant surgeon' in 1799. After about two decades in the Company's employ he resigned in 1818 with £40,000 – a sum he could never have made from medical practice alone. He subsequently sat in Parliament as an 'advanced Radical', held several prestigious positions (such as the lord rectorship of Marishal College, Aberdeen, examiner of candidates for the Company's medical service, and personal physician to the Duke of Wellington) and incidentally devoted his leisure time to the task of translating Dante's *Inferno*.[11]

Large-scale embezzlement and considerable earnings from hospital contracts were endemic among the medical profession in India, and asylum owners and superintendents were not immune. Valentine Conolly in Madras, who not only established and owned the local lunatic asylum, but also acted as its medical superintendent (with questionable zeal), while simultaneously holding the influential position of member of the very medical board which was supposed to thwart corrupt practices, is the most successful example. However, surgeons Fitzgerald and Dalton, his successors, also gained reasonable prosperity by engaging in a practice that had been condemned by the general public and medical officers in England, and had eventually (from 1823 onwards) been disallowed by the Company.[12] Fitzgerald and subsequently Dalton had bought the asylum building together with the charge of the lunatics for a price three times above the premises' estimated value, and had, after a few years, realized considerable profit. The East India Company, once alerted to these facts, strongly disapproved of the practice of trading in asylums, and the Madras government consequently passed orders which disallowed it for the future.

In the middle of the nineteenth century members of the medical profession were apparently not always in favour of profiteering by buying and selling medical practices and madhouses. Forbes Winslow, editor of the *Journal of Psychological Medicine* and president of the association of medical officers of asylums and hospitals for the insane in England (who himself owned two private lunatic asylums in London), succinctly underlined the organized medical profession's concern. He complained in 1858 that asylums and their inmates could be 'brought into the market and offered for sale, like a flock of sheep, to the highest bidder'.[13] It was however not so much the fact of the monetary transaction itself, that Winslow found disturbing, but the way in which it was carried out. The sale, he asserted, was undertaken 'in a manner calculated to destroy all public confidence and trust, in the honesty, integrity, and even common respectability of those connected with similar institutions'. And what is more, private madhouse proprietors would not always be what John Conolly in 1830 called 'respectable, well-educated and humane individuals', often having instead a lower-class background, not considered to be conducive to showing kindness and humanity toward the people in their charge. 'The patients are transmitted', Conolly asserted 'like stock in trade, from one member of the family to another, and from one generation to another; they come in youth to the father, they linger out their age with the son'.[14]

In a similar vein the medical board of Bengal in 1836 inveighed against the continued existence of 'Beardsmore's Bedlam'. Beardsmore was after all no medical doctor, having previously served as a soldier, and being described by the board's medical officers as 'an industrious but uneducated man' who 'pretended to no medical knowledge, [who] has never claimed the merit of originating any sort of improvement'.[15] The tug-of-war between medical board and private madhouse owner went public several times, as Beardsmore was not inclined to have his business jeopardized. After all, he had 'no other means of subsistence but what he derive[d] from superintending' his private asylum.[16] The province's most influential medicos for their part were of the opinion that Beardsmore should at the very least be made to recognize that he was their 'subordinate' – and should preferably be stripped of the charge of public patients altogether.

The very fact that a medically unqualified individual with a lower-class background was allowed by the Company's authorities to manage an institution, was a challenge to the board's authority. J. Sawers, the board's secretary, asserted as early as 1820, dryly and with the acerbic calmness of those confident in their own superiority: 'I disapprove of your Institution altogether, Sir'.[17] He did his utmost to make life difficult for Beardsmore by attempting to reclassify patients and demanding changes in the prevailing staff structure. Sawers certainly nurtured a personal grudge against Beardsmore. His own private madhouse had been declared to be a 'damp, sultry and gloomy place', beyond repair.[18] Government decided, against Sawers' contrary assertion that his premises were 'a very dry and comfortable habitation',[19] to have all public patients removed from there. The patients were finally admitted into the private asylum run by Beardsmore and a surgeon Robinson!

Despite the personal undercurrents in the clash between Beardsmore and surgeon Sawers, the 'Beardsmore affair' was also a manifestation of a more general concern among the medical profession of the period. The members of the medical board feared that their authority as experts and controlling agents in matters medical might be undermined by interlopers such as Beardsmore. They further claimed that the involvement of the laity in the private 'mad-business' would bring the medical profession into disrepute. In short, the medical board of Bengal as much as Winslow in England, and many other asylum superintendents, were anxious lest 'guilt by association' adversely affect the medical professionals' still shaky reputation and status.

In India practitioners' fear of being tainted by shady and avaricious medicos of doubtful expertise became more widespread once the Company took the first steps to check its employees' multiple pursuits of profit from non-medical or corrupt activities, and had more clearly formulated the standards of formal and practical qualification required on entry to the medical services. In 1826 officers in the Bengal army, for example, were forbidden to engage in commercial speculation (whilst those in civil employ were, until 1841, left to make the most of the East's bounty). Commissioned Company servants were in general paid relatively generous salaries, and from 1842 received increased pensions. Medical staff were also required to be, if not experienced, than at least qualified in the practice of the healing arts – rather than being sponsored by a Company director or having merely purchased a commission in one of London's coffee houses.

From 1822 onwards candidates had to produce a diploma from one of the Royal Colleges of Surgeons (of London, Dublin, or Edinburgh), or the College and University or the Faculty of Physicians and Surgeons of Glasgow. In addition they were required to undergo examination by the Company's physician in London, to attend a course of lectures in 'Hindoostanee', and, from 1828 onwards, advised to take with them to India a copy of J. Annesley's pioneering reference book *Researches into the causes, nature and treatment of the more prevalent diseases of India.*[20] Medical service in India was to become a professional career rather than a scramble for wealth. The introduction of competitive exams in 1855 set the seal on this process.

The Company's policy of discouraging corruption and mediocre medical practice by paying handsome salaries, granting pensions, and tightening standards for entry into the medical service certainly led to a better qualified and more reliable breed of medical servant applying for positions in the East toward the middle of the century. Misappropriation of hospital funds occurred with reduced frequency, and the quality of patient care, and with it of Company doctors' reputation, seem to have risen slowly. Medical officers in India themselves played an important part in this process. They founded their own professional lobbies in order to assert their expertise and knowledge and to defend their interests against 'interlopers' (especially against those without formal medical training or practising in one of the classical Indian traditions such as *yunani* and *ayurveda*).[21]

There existed however as yet no organized interest group lobbying the specific case of those engaged in the management and treatment of the mad in India (such as the association of asylum superintendents in England). Nor was 'asylum science' or the treatment of the mad amongst the subjects with which candidates for the medical service had to be familiar.[22] Lunatic asylums were usually only one amongst many of an assistant surgeon's (and, rarely, of a surgeon's) charges. Towards the middle of the century – when asylums had grown bigger – a medical officer's other duties were to be more restricted and he would spend more time within the asylum compound. Yet he still usually only held the office of asylum superintendent for a short period. W. Campbell, who had been superintendent of the Bombay asylum for about fifteen years was certainly an exception. Once a medico was promoted he would relinquish his former tasks and a new officer would take his place. On average he would be in charge of a lunatic asylum for only about two years before he was promoted to a better paid and more reputable position. One consequence of such high staff turnover in asylums was that superintendents found it hard to take much interest in the part of their duty that still carried with it so many negative connotations. Acting superintendents tended to confine themselves to carrying out the minimum required, leaving the day-to-day management of the place to their subordinates, especially when the premises themselves happened to be in a state nearing dereliction.

Lack of specialization and high staff turnover were however not confined to the lunacy-sector. The range of any Company medico's duties was in general very different from that of a medical officer working in Britain. In 1841 J. M'Cosh, former graduate of the Royal College of Surgeons, Edinburgh, and lecturer in clinical medicine at the New Medical College, Calcutta, emphasized some of the peculiarities of service under the Company in his *Medical Advice to the Indian Stranger*. 'In India, no distinction is made', he held, 'between the practice of medicine and surgery'.[23] Consequently, 'every officer must act in either capacity, as circumstances demand', and must be willing to 'exercise his profession in the most comprehensive sense of the word'. Specialization in a particular branch of medicine or surgery (and, eventually, in psychiatry) had in contrast become increasingly common in Europe, and, what is more, often constituted the necessary precondition for a medico's rise to fame and wealth. This was not yet the case for the ordinary Company doctor.

When medical officers in India did gain a reputation for specialized achievements, it was more often in the domain of biology, ethnology, or due to their linguistic skills, rather than in the subject of medicine or surgery in its more narrow sense. Many early nineteenth-century doctors were keen travellers and collectors of plants and artefacts. A few even wrote dictionaries of Indian languages or provided accounts and drew sketches of tribal customs. Such pursuits were, however, usually leisure-time activities rather than part of a medico's official duty, and (apart from sometimes ensuring a lasting reputation) might be instrumental in counteracting those 'dangers of ennuie and hypochondriasis' to which Dr M'Cosh expressly alerted the 'Indian Stranger'.[24] These non-medical specialities fitted the image of what a surgeon's task in the East was commonly seen to imply. He was not only expected to engage in his 'more regular duties', but 'as occasion presents itself' should 'act the part of aurist, oculist, accoucheur, chemist, and medical jurist'. 'But this is not enough', warned M'Cosh the unwary newcomer,

> he ought to be able to physic his own horse or dog, superintend the construction of his own house, or boat, or baggage-waggon, know how to grow green-peas and cauliflowers, how to fatten capons and sucking-pigs, how to make jug-soup and tapioca, how to shoot wild-geese, ride a steeple-chase, drive a cabriolet, and sail a cutter, how to balance the debtor and creditor side of his monthly-accounts to the utmost farthing, how to calculate half-batta in vulgar and decimal fractions, and how to argue, logically, against retrenchments.[25]

The early part of the nineteenth century, then, was the period when the medical profession began to flex its muscles, and assert its professional authority – in British India as much as in Britain. In regard to the practice of what later came to be labelled 'psychiatry', however, the process of medical professionalization in British India lagged considerably behind developments in Europe. Madness had certainly become medicalized in that the European insane were subject to medical attention rather than being simply left to the charge of the police authorities. (Nor could the insane be looked after by their own relatives who would in most cases have been in

Britain, nor be cared for by missionaries, as was the case in German colonial territories in Africa toward the beginning of the twentieth century.) However, Company surgeons came in a variety of guises, with different social backgrounds, diverse qualifications, ambitions, and approaches. And the care of the insane affected their other commitments to a highly differing extent.

For example, contrast the basis of surgeon Conolly's reputation with that of surgeon Cantor. Conolly certainly belonged to the 'old breed' of Company servants, who came to India in search of fortune, found it, and returned home to Britain to enjoy their retirement in ease and luxury. They did usually not excel in anything of a strictly professional kind, although they might be remembered for those activities that gained them their wealth (as, in Conolly's case, the establishment of Madras's first madhouse). Cantor in contrast was of a completely different stripe. He took up medical practice as a career in itself rather than merely as a conduit to trade and financial speculation. He was regarded by his colleagues on the medical board as a competent practitioner and had got as close to recognition as an expert in the treatment of the mad as any medical officer in India in the period. He had been superintendent of the lunatic asylum in Penang, had published a report on his work there, and was, on transfer to India, entrusted with re-organizing the hitherto privately managed Calcutta lunatic asylum. He also superintended and reformed the 'native' lunatic asylum in Dhalanda. Cantor was not unaware of his prominent position as the province's first, officially acknowledged expert in lunacy. He proudly cited his experience in South East Asia, and frequently referred knowledgeably to asylum management as practised in England and France, though never failing to point out that circumstances in India demanded some modification of treatment principles.

What made the career of Conolly and that of Cantor so different owed much to the fact that the former had established his fame at a period when becoming a 'navab' was still seen as a normal and legitimate aspiration. Cantor, in contrast, took up practice in the East when not only the standards of his own profession but also those of the East India Company demanded that medical officers should be reasonably well qualified, and should devote their time and energy primarily to their medical duties. However, although Conolly and Cantor may easily be juxtaposed as ideal examples of the gradual shift from mere pecuniary gain to the beginnings of medical profession-alization, there are also examples of asylum doctors who would not readily fit into this dichotomy. The world of medical practice was as yet neither ordered nor standardized. Surgeon Dick, for example, owned a madhouse in Bengal around the time Conolly left Madras. Dick was a successful entrepreneur in the 'mad-business'. Yet he was equally adept at gaining fame as a medical doctor. Back in England he assured himself of various reputable medical appointments and even became examiner of the Company's candidates for the medical service.

On the other hand, one of Cantor's contemporaries in Bombay failed to gain official recognition as a specialist in lunacy – despite his determined efforts to convince the provincial medical and government authorities of his superior expertise. Surgeon W. Campbell held the position of asylum superintendent from 1849 to 1864, and had been greatly devoted to the care of his European patients. He undoubtedly saw himself as an expert on insanity. But rather than subscribing to a narrowly medical model of madness, his approach was more broadly based upon principles of 'moral therapy'. He recognized, though, the need for specialist training and consequently suggested that he be sent to Europe to make himself familiar with the most modern principles of asylum management and psychological medicine. His request was however declined and he consequently pottered on in the Bombay asylum as a mad-doctor. Campbell had made the mistake of specializing in a marginalized area of medicine before he had consolidated his position as a practitioner in general (and before he had made friends among the more influential individuals of Bombay's professional bodies).

Dr W. Arbuckle, in contrast, who preceded him in the charge of the Bombay lunatic asylum, had a completely different understanding as to what asylum superintendence would entail for his own career. Arbuckle had himself elected onto various professional bodies, such as the Medical and Physical Society of Bombay. The superintendency of the Bombay lunatic asylum was for him only one, instrumental, step in his career. He was familiar with the mainstream ideas in the treatment of the insane, but unlike Campbell he subscribed to a more narrowly medical model. This orientation fitted in well with his general ambitions as one of the town's most renowned medical practitioners. The professional kudos that could be gained was, so it seems, very much dependent on the particular branch of medicine a doctor was in, and the superintendence of madhouses was not one of the positions that would necessarily by itself ensure a rise in social and professional status.

The medicalization of madness

The impression that emerges from an examination of various asylum superintendents' careers over the first half of the nineteenth century is not only one of increasing professionalization, but also of a process of the medicalization of madness. However, doctors were not yet fully successful, it appears, in establishing with the Company's authorities in India the necessity of an exclusively medical authority in the management of the mad. It has already been noted that the lunatic asylum in Calcutta had been owned and managed by a non-medico for more than three decades (despite repeated protests by the local medical authorities). When in 1856 Dr J. Cantor was finally authorized to take over the charge of the Beardsmores' asylum, the seal of medical supremacy in the treatment of the insane in British India's main centres was set. However, only slowly was the care for the mentally ill to become universally acknowledged as an area of medical science requiring specialist skills. Cantor's appointment could nevertheless be seen to mark a movement away from the conviction that the care of the mad was merely a 'difficult' and 'peculiar' task, to the opinion that the mentally ill could only be looked after by specialists with broad medical qualifications.

Contrasting assessments of the state of the art towards the second half of the nineteenth century point up the lack of professional unison. J.C. Bucknill and D.H. Tuke, authors of the *Manual of Psychological Medicine*, for example, optimistically asserted in 1858 that 'a knowledge of the nature and treatment of Insanity is now expected of every well-educated man'.[26] On a more pessimistic, and arguably more realistic note, J.M. Granville, the author of *The Care and Cure of the Insane*, still held in 1877 that the 'lack of acquaintance with lunacy is extraordinary. The great body of medical men appear to know scarcely more of arrangements and methods of treatment adopted in asylums than the general public'.

One factor which slowed down the process of medicalization was the emergence of a new paradigm for the treatment of the mentally ill: the doctrine of 'moral therapy'. This approach was based on the assumption that the insane were essentially human, though lacking in self-control and discipline. By substituting physical restraint and punishment by kindness and moral education, the Tukes, the main protagonists of moral therapy in Britain, had achieved great fame. Most pertinently, however, the Tukes' kind and humane – albeit paternalistic – mode of treatment was fuelled by their Quakerism rather than by any medical expertise. Their success in the treatment of fellow Quakers in the York Retreat constituted therefore, as Bynum has pointed out, a 'damning attack on the medical profession's capacity to deal with mental illness'.[27] The Tukes' regime could produce high recovery rates, whilst the medical profession had hardly any comparable achievements to show. Similarly, G. Higgins (a magistrate in York, who was instrumental in uncovering abuse of inmates in the local asylum, and contributed to a significant decrease of patients' deaths by helping to establish a system of lay visitations and public control) asserted that hardly anybody could doubt the superior efficacy of the peculiar 'medicine' advocated by him, namely 'visitors and committees'. He made the challenging point that public supervision of asylum affairs alone would do more than, for example, 'Dr Hunter's famous secret *insane powders* – either green or grey – or his patent Brazil salts'.[28]

Even doctors themselves had to admit that medicine's success in treating insanity was very restricted. Dr Thomas Monro, for long an acknowledged expert in the medical treatment of the insane in his capacity as physician to Bethlem Hospital, felt compelled to concede before the select committee on the better regulation of madhouses in England in 1815, that insanity 'is not cured by medicine'.[29] The important point that had emerged in England at the beginning of the nineteenth century was that (as Bynum aptly put it) 'if physicians *qua* physician could do nothing for the lunatic except treat his bodily afflictions, then the medical man had no special claim to a unique place in the treatment of mental illness'.[30] Moreover, as a consequence, doctors' 'income, prestige, and medical theories were all threatened.'

In British India the medical profession was of course in principle faced with these same dilemmas. The idea of 'moral therapy' and the news of the Tukes' success in treating the insane almost without restraint or recourse to medical nostrums, reached the British community in India towards the turn of the century. The provinces' medical boards responded by asserting that whilst kindness and humanity were essential in the management of the mad, lack of medical expertise would have harmful effects. After all, insanity was believed to be a disease of the brain. This claim that madness was in the last instance somatic seemed to justify medical dominance in the treatment of its sufferers.

The way in which the medical profession in British India chose to reconcile the non-medical dogma of humane and kind treatment with their interest in 'income, prestige, and medical theories' was therefore by acknowledging the partial importance of 'moral therapy', whilst at the same time strongly rejecting the slogan that 'management did more than medicine'.[31] This approach is again highlighted by the Bengal medical board's allegations against Beardsmore, whose 'plan of moral treatment' it considered inadequate in that it not only lacked the 'intimate and . . . cultivated experience of the varied forms and shades of mental diseases as well as a more enlarged philanthropy' which were seen to be so 'indispensable' in asylum management, but was also 'unaided and uncontrolled by the Ordinary medical Attendant'.[32] When in 1855 the board's submission that it was 'on the whole advisable to dispense with' the asylum owner's services was accepted by the government, the medical profession had at long last succeeded in asserting its authority.[33]

The subordination of 'native' medicine

Company surgeons' rise to professional authority was fraught with obstacles and endless struggles for power, as is evidenced by the almost continual dispute between Beardsmore and the various members of the Bengal medical board. A further factor that tended to provoke European medical experts' competitive spirit and social and racial snobbery, was largely related to the typically colonial order of things: the fact that a European ruling elite had established itself as superior to those it regarded as its native colonial subjects. The European community in general had developed a distaste for people of Indian and mixed race – and doctors were not free from such prejudice. Company surgeons frequently expressed their unease about the presence of a great number of non-Europeans in the Indian medical department.

They in fact had ample scope for venting their racial sentiments, as Eurasians, for example, would usually be assigned to every European regiment as apothecaries and stewards, working under a European surgeon. (Admittedly, in some cases Europeans, too, took up such positions. But they were usually 'the sons of sergeants or soldiers, who have not had the advantage of a European education'.[34] In view of their lower-class background, and deprived of the supposed blessings that British education was supposed to impart, they too would be almost exclusively relegated to subordinate positions.) Indian practitioners or 'native doctors' however got the worst of racial and social discrimination. They were permitted to take up only a restricted range of very inferior positions in the Company's employ, and usually worked as assistants to European medical officers in charge of 'native troops', hospitals, or jails.

Medical practices that were based on the eminent classical traditions of the Hindu (ayurveda) and Islamic (yunani) arts of healing, of course, continued to be relevant to the majority of people in India at this period. So were those medical traditions which were based in healing temples, and were commonly (and usually derogatively) described by the western as well as the ayurvedic and yunani scientific communities as 'folk medicine' (practised by healers such as fakirs, maulanas, ojash, pujaris, and pandits). Among the European community, the politically and ideologically dominant group in British India, any other than 'modern' European medical practice was regarded with contempt.

Although banished to the lower orders of medical practice, subordinate members of the Company's medical department still posed a potential threat to a professional clique eager to consolidate its own, still precarious position. Even those medical officers who were convinced of the unquestionable superiority of European medicine, had to concede (if not without derogatory asides) that not only did 'some medicines', prescribed by Indian practitioners, work with 'great efficacy' and that they were administered 'occasionally with success', but that some operations were practised 'with more skill than from their very rude instruments could be anticipated'.[35] Even in regard to the method of Indian inoculation, disparaged by the authorities, some European medicos admitted that 'not more than one percent die' in consequence of its application.

The acknowledgement (however reluctant and circumspect) that indigenous medicine and its practitioners could often be effective and successful tended to fuel the ever-growing hostile response towards them. The fierceness with which the campaign against all eastern healing systems was fought during the 1830s by the majority of European medical practitioners can at least partly be accounted for by an underlying feeling of threat, and awareness of western medicine's relative impotence in the face of high disease and mortality rates. The sway of European medicine was asserted, symbolically as much as practically, by having the formal mainstays of organized medical practice in British India, the provinces' medical schools, transformed into training schools on a par with colleges in Britain, rather than with traditional medical education in India. In Calcutta, for example, where indigenous as well as western medicine was taught at the Sanskrit College and the Madrassa, lectures in Urdu were scrapped, and students were instructed in English in anatomy, chemistry, surgery, materia-medica, physics, and practical dissection by professors trained in Britain.

Despite these efforts to 'spread the light of European knowledge and civilization' among 'native' and Eurasian candidates for the medical service, suspicion as to the new converts' loyalty to western ways was widespread. J. M'Cosh, who had lectured in clinical medicine at what had been baptized the *new* medical college in Calcutta exclaimed, for example, in 1841 that he was 'inclined to think very favourably' of his students' 'zeal, of their capacity, and of their attainments'.[36] Yet he added, that his

> only fears were, that the want of integrity, so general in the Native character, would, notwithstanding their enlight-ened education, still cling to them as their birthright; and that, on any trying emergency, or dangerous personal illness, they would distrust their European doctrines, and resort to their national empyricism, or to superstitious invocation of the deities of their fathers.

The colonialist's task was, it seems, not an easy one. Medical officers were not to be spared the disappointment of those very pupils who had been ridded of a 'mere combination of quackery and superstition'[37] by laboriously imparted western knowledge, easily reverting to their 'native ways'. The mere conviction that western medicine was best, was in a colonial setting sufficient to forcefully (and in the opinion of the European rulers, legitimately) establish its supremacy. The gradual marginalization of Eurasian and Indian practitioners and their subordination to western medical practices was only one component of this process.

The general atmosphere created by advancing European medicine, of course, also pervaded British India's madhouses. In these specialized institutions, too, change was discernible, although the medical treatment and the general management of the insane was but tangentially affected. After all, the responsibility for European patients had always been with a European superintendent. Only in 'native lunatic asylums' were Indian assistants customarily entrusted with the day-to-day care of Indian and lower-class Eurasian patients (but even there a European had always been authorized to control the way in which Indian inmates were treated). A general order of 1826 then expressly stipulated that 'Half-castes and other natives . . . be confined to subordinate offices'.[38] Ever since the establishment of lunatic asylums in India it had however been a problem to attract reliable European employees. In consequence of the new, race-specific regulation, asylum superintendents found it even more difficult to enlist, for example, apothecaries who were racially acceptable, as well as being suitable for their task in terms of their character, qualification, or experience. Subordinate staff, and in particular asylum keepers or attendants, were extremely poorly paid, and work in a *pagal-khana* or madhouse did not appeal to many.

As in Britain, those attending on the mentally ill would frequently be 'such as are unable to obtain places elsewhere',[39] or as Scull put it, be drawn from 'the dregs of society'.[40] Staff turnover rates were high, superintendents' complaints numerous, and the government authorities' displeasure with subordinate medical staff's and keepers' unreliability evident. Despite problems in inducing Europeans or Eurasians 'of a respectable class' to take up subordinate positions in the provincial capitals' asylums, the Company would not even consider changing its recruitment policy. Indians were excluded, no matter how badly equipped European and

Eurasian aspirant apothecaries, overseers, stewards, and matrons were for their job.

Although asylum staff were considered by protagonists of 'moral therapy' to be 'most essential instruments',[41] super-intendents were primarily concerned with establishing that expert medical management was the most essential factor in the treatment of the insane. Medical officers would, of course, insist (albeit mostly unsuccessfully) that they be authorized to employ a sufficient number of staff in order to guarantee the security and day-to-day care of patients. At the same time they preferred to pass on orders to European and Eurasian staff of inferior abilities and of doubtful character, rather than supervising Indian employees.

Hierarchical regulation of employment such as that introduced by surgeon Cantor in Calcutta consequently rendered the lower strata among the staff (the 'native establishment') almost as subordinate to the whims of their European superiors and the constraints of a hierarchically structured institution as the patients they were supposed to care for. It appears then that, although, in general, problems in the recruitment and management of subordinate staff similar to those that prevailed in the majority of asylums in Britain were also present in India, racial discrimination specific to the European asylum in colonial India exacerbated the staff problems.

Medicine and Empire

Another feature intrinsically linked with the fact that employees of the East India Company worked within a colonial setting, was the peculiar career structure of officers in the Indian medical service. The most crucial difference from that of medical practitioners working in private practice or in public hospitals in Britain was that medical men in India automatically held a commission when joining the service. They would usually enter employment with the Company as ensign (or lieutenant) *and* assistant surgeon. When promoted they had to decide in which branch to continue their career, but they were in any case subject to recall to military duty. Changes of position and re-appointments occurred frequently. These were occasioned mainly by the high fatality rate among Company servants, and fluctuating manpower demand arising from the engagement of the Company's European army in various wars and 'punitive expeditions' during the earlier part of the nineteenth century. Medical officers in India consequently had much less freedom in deciding where to practise than their colleagues in Britain. They also did not have the possibility of opting out of assignment to any specific regiment, even when they found the duties and lifestyle of an army doctor unpalatable.

The strong link between the practice of medicine and the activities of the military in India had implications that went far beyond individual doctors' discomfiture. It also serves, as Arnold pointed out, 'as a reminder of the enduring importance of the army within the British colonial system in India', and, what is more, underlines the fact that the doctor 'who practised among the European soldiery . . . bore a formidable responsibility for the maintenance of British military power in India'.[42]

What concerned the medical officers newly arrived from England most, however, was the immediate practical and mundane implications of their 'formidable responsibility'. If they were lucky they would not straight away have to face up to the wide range of professional tasks of a civil surgeon or regimental doctor, and to the unfamiliar duties that, according to Dr M'Cosh, life in the East demanded. If there was no urgent need associated with epidemic or warfare, the newly commissioned assistant surgeon would spend a couple of months at one of the general hospitals acclimatising himself to the formal requirements of his new position, and getting habituated to 'the diseases peculiar to the country, and the treatment put in practice'.[43] The chance of becoming familiar with the more ubiquitous diseases afflicting the town's European citizens was however at times somewhat restricted. The general hospital in Calcutta, for example, practised a socially and racially discriminatory admissions policy via high charges, thereby reducing not only its usefulness for the general European public but also its scope as a training school.

The young assistant would nevertheless soon pick up general custom and practice. Being initiated to the Company's medical service (regardless of the branch in which he was finally to end up), after all also implied that the trainee had to 'consider himself in the vortex of Indian society'.[44] 'Indian' society was here meant to refer to the ways peculiar to both the European expatriate and the indigenous communities. A newcomer was therefore required to 'conform to the manners and customs of his compatriots' and was expected to 'submit to the numerous prejudices of caste among the Natives, and be contented' (although old India hands themselves would rarely live up to these imperatives). He was to be 'constantly upon his guard against anger, for he will have much to irritate him'. And 'on no account' was he to 'give way to beating his servants, a practice too common amongst new-comers'.

India was considered by many 'a dreadfully difficult country',[45] and its strange ways and customs (not only of the Indian, but also of the European communities) were a trial for the uninitiated and faint of heart. This was true as much for the officer and civil servant as for the soldier and sailor, for the doctor as much as for the patient in the madhouse. Moreover, disease would hit the medico as badly as it affected his officer-colleagues (whose privileges, lifestyle, and habits he shared), and 'the cloud of melancholy' could hover over the tent or compound of the surgeon as thickly as over his patients'. The fact that disease and even madness also struck the very experts who were supposed to maintain the health and sanity of others, tended to strengthen the belief among civilians and soldiers that the preservation of one's health in the tropics was more dependent on 'God's providence' or the healing and preventive powers of alcoholic spirits, tobacco, exercise, warm clothing, or devices such as the 'cholera belt', than on the expertise of trained medical practitioners.

Moreover, European doctors generally lacked the means and skills necessary to ameliorate the condition of what a royal commission called the 'sickly army in India'.[46] European medical science was in the early nineteenth century not yet in a position to boast much success in the cure of the most common diseases among Europeans in India. Nor were its methods of pain relief and of symptomatic treatment all that effective. It is true that the discovery of a vaccine against smallpox, for example, helped to reduce the number of fatalities from a disease that had been endemic in certain parts of India. And the disdain and scorn bestowed on Indian *tikadars* (who had for centuries performed inoculation against smallpox) by Company authorities and the public at large certainly attest to the fact that by around the 1830s European science and medicine had come to be perceived as the paragon of knowledge and civilization. J.R. Martin voiced in 1835 a wide-spread conviction when he exclaimed that

> the diffusion of European medical science, with its collateral branches, must prove one of the most direct and impressive modes of demonstrating to the natives, the superiority of European knowledge in general, and that they must cultivate it actively if they would rise in the scale of nations.[47]

However, despite the fervour and zeal occasionally exhibited in attempts to eradicate 'superstition' and 'bigotry' in Indian medical systems, and the success of vaccination campaigns among Europeans, western medicine performed but poorly within the context of the Company's Raj in India. Cholera, for example (which accounted between 1830 and 1846 for about 10 per cent of deaths among the British in Bombay,[48] and between 1818 and 1854 killed more than 8,500 British soldiers[49]), was not for decades to be successfully checked. Similarly the hazards of 'fevers' and 'dysentry and diarrhoea', which killed on average about one quarter and one third of the sick, respectively, was only to be ameliorated towards the beginning of the twentieth century. The health of army servants in particular was notoriously bad during the early decades, with a mortality rate from disease seven times higher than that from wartime casualties. Soldiers would consequently maintain that it was in most cases 'disease, and not the enemy that killed' their comrades.[50] Against the various forms of madness, too, medical doctors could do little but help to ameliorate patients' physical condition and refer them to the care of practitioners in England.

Admittedly, the extremely bad state of health of army personnel in India (which even by the middle of the century would occasion mortality rates more than double those among the military in Britain) was not entirely to be blamed on a failure of European medicine or of its representatives. Nor did there exist any effective medicine that would cure insanity. Death was more common among the lower ranks, and was closely linked with unsanitary and cheerless living conditions, inadequate diet, and abuse of the liquor bottle. The question of life and death was consequently not one that could easily be ap-

proached by a medical practitioner alone. This fact was acknowledged and indeed emphasized by the royal commission on the
sanitary state of the army in India in their summary statement
that

> it is necessary to bear in mind that the soldier's health in
> India, as elsewhere, is the product of all the conditions to
> which he is exposed. It is not solely the result of climate,
> nor of locality and dwelling place, nor of diet, habits, nor
> duties; it is the product of all of these.[51]

Yet despite the admission that a combination of factors would
affect 'the soldier's health' and the fact that medical officers
would see many more of their patients die than they could
restore to health, the role of the doctor was perceived by the
Company's authorities to be indispensable – regardless of the
particular branch in which he practised. Medicine and its
practitioners gradually gained prestige and status at a period
and in circumstances, so it seems, when the medical profession
was (in terms of cure rates, and symptomatic and pain relief)
not particularly successful in the practice of its trade.
Considering therefore that medical officers in the East India
Company's employ were faced with an enormous incidence of
disease, and with unsalubrious and stressful living conditions,
whilst lacking the drug technology of later decades (such as
penicillin) that would have allowed for instant cures, they did
not so badly in asserting their position as the ultimate authority
in matters of healing.

It was above all during these early decades of the nineteenth
century that the foundation for the enduring great colonial
medical myth was laid. The medical doctor was to become a
major pillar of European colonial ideology in that his services
for the good of humankind were seen to legitimate foreign rule
and to serve as proof of the unquestionable superiority of
western civilization in general. This conviction was expressed
frequently (most succinctly by Martin in the 1830s), and even as
recently as 1950, when D. MacDonald, a former member of the
Indian Medical Service, and author of *Surgeons Twoe and a
Barber. Being Some Account of the Life and Work of the Indian Medical
Service* would place in the front pages of his book Marshal H.
Lyautey's epigram that 'the doctor is the sole excuse for
colonization'.

111

Those who cared for the mentally ill in British India were not always necessarily medical doctors. When medical practitioners became professionalized, and distanced themselves from the trade in sickness, medically trained asylum superintendents lagged behind, as they failed to convince government and medical authorities of their special professional skills. By mid-century, however, the medicalization of madness in India was all but complete, as western expertise in care of the sick in mind joined that of the sick in body as a significant component of the apparatus for imposing the enlightened nostrums of European civilization upon colonial India – at the expense of indigenous skills.

4

The patients

'Highly irregular conduct' and 'neglect of duty'

In early spring 1845 a young officer of the Indian Navy, by the name of Edward Charles Zouch, was embarked on the *Imam of Muscat*, on account of his deranged state of mind. Lieutenant Zouch had been granted a sick certificate that entitled him to three years furlough in England. He had served on various of the Company's vessels in India since April 1830, and was put on the sicklist in July 1844 in consequence of his broken health on return from a naval mission to the Persian Gulf. At that stage of his career the then 28-year-old was keen to see (at least for a while) the last of duty in India, and yearned to be allowed to proceed to Europe on sick leave. However, he was thwarted in this by Company authorities anxious to relieve the navy's pressing manpower needs by keeping its men in service as long as possible. In consequence Zouch developed symptoms of 'mania' or, as the certifying doctor in Bombay put it, on the refusal of sick-leave 'his mental symptoms seem to have supervened'.[1]

On further investigation by a medical committee set up to decide on the authenticity and severity of Zouch's mental symptoms, several earlier instances were recollected by fellow-officers when Lieutenant Zouch had behaved somewhat oddly. While on duty on one of the Company's receiving ships, for example, 'his Conduct had attracted the notice of every one on board'.[2] Not only did he walk 'the deck night, and day successively', but he also one morning 'fancied that he was to be hanged at eight o'clock' and 'attended punctually for the purpose and behaved in the most extravagant manner, when

Figure 6 View of Bombay Harbour, taken from the Island of Kolaba, 1833. (Reproduced by permission of the India Office Library and Records and the British Library, London.)

the hour passed and his anticipation had not been realized'. It further transpired that Zouch had 'always been considered by the officers of his own Service as being of unsound mind', and many more corroborative events were related to the committee. One event in particular had created amusement and bewilderment alike. On board a ship, Zouch had 'imagined himself transformed into a vegetable, an artichoke, and was in the habit of taking advantage of every shower, that fell in order that he might be properly watered'.

On the basis of this evidence Lieutenant Zouch was seen as a fit subject for the province's lunatic asylum, and was, in September 1844, admitted to the mental institution on the Kolaba peninsula as a maniac with a melancholic trait. After only a couple of months he was reported to have fallen into 'a state of confirmed idiocy'. In the absence of any significant improvement in mental symptoms, Zouch was finally recommended for transfer to Europe.

Apart from his somewhat unusual and charming episode as an artichoke, Zouch's case shares certain characteristics with several of his fellow inmates' in the asylum's first-class apartments, and even some on the second-class wards. To begin with, a great number of the mad had previously suffered from a variety of physical illnesses. They would frequently have been subject to medical treatment, either (in the case of military or naval personnel) in one of the regimental or port hospitals or else (in the case of civilians or high-ranking officers) in the general hospital or at their own homes under the civil surgeon's professional attention.

Private Timothy Crawley of the second European regiment and formerly a labourer in Ireland, for example, was admitted to the Calcutta lunatic asylum in June 1841, supposedly suffering from 'mania periodica'.[3] Just a few months previously, in February, he had been admitted into the regimental hospital with 'febrile symptoms and a quick and hot pulse attended with delirium, having made an attempt to drown himself'. A year later, in August 1842, gunner Patrick Lane, formerly a weaver of Cork, Ireland, joined the patients in the Calcutta second-class ward.[4] He too had a recent history of physical ailments. He had been admitted to the regimental hospital for pain in the back of the head, chronic hepatitis, and 'symptomatic affections of the Intestines'. When 'symptoms of mental aberration' were observed, he was transferred to the province's madhouse. He was diagnosed as suffering from 'Theo Mania' due to his persistent 'delusion that he beheld visions, and had conversations with the Allmighty'. At around the same time, in 1843, another Irishman, private James Brady, was admitted to the asylum in Madras.[5] He, too, had been sent to his regiment's hospital some months previously, when he suffered from delirium tremens, and subsequently from an attack of fever. And finally, gunner Thomas Hanlon of the Horse Artillery having suffered 'two severe falls from his horse at riding drill', was treated in the local hospital, and on exhibition of mental symptoms was transferred to the lunatic asylum.[6]

Hospitalization on account of accidents, fever, syphilis, cholera, diarrhoea, and delirium tremens was certainly one experience commonly shared by most asylum inmates. Similarly common was inmates' previous experience of disciplinary punishment: verbal reprimand, downgrading in rank, tightened drill, and solitary confinement. Only some five years before Lieutenant Zouch, for example, turned into a vegetable, he had been court-martialled in Bombay Harbour and reprimanded for 'most disgraceful and highly irregular conduct and neglect of duty to the prejudice of good order and naval discipline'.[7] Zouch, then a midshipman, was ordered to assume temporary charge of the Company's steam vessel *Atalanta* moored in Bombay Harbour, and had failed to keep control of the situation when the ship had caught fire. Various other superior officers had rushed to the burning vessel and had taken over command from him. An argument ensued during which Zouch had been accused by the other officers of being too drunk to perform his duty, and that, looking highly agitated, he was unable to manage the confusion on the burning ship.

For his superiors Zouch's excited behaviour was doubtlessly attributable to intoxication and was censured as having been 'most disgraceful' and 'highly irregular'. Although Zouch was eventually not found guilty of drunkenness by a court martial, the commander of the local forces and government strongly disapproved of 'both the verdict and the award'[8] and felt

> imperatively called on to counteract as far as possible, the serious evil that must result to the respectability, general efficiency, and well-being of the Indian Navy, were such an

aggravated breach of duty, as is presented in the case under consideration, permitted to pass by unnoticed.[9]

The maintenance of discipline and the reputation of the service were given priority both over the process of the law, and over the mercy for which Zouch pleaded in his defence speech. Zouch was to be made an example of, especially in the light of what was perceived to be 'the insubordinate and unmilitary feeling which prevails among many of the junior members of the Indian Navy'.

Undisciplined behaviour and neglect of duty could never be taken lightly within the military, and many a junior officer, but, even more common, soldiers were subjected to the harsh consequences of military discipline. Zouch suffered considerable social embarrassment in consequence of the *Atalanta* affair, although he was spared the even more humiliating experience of incarceration or prolonged suspension from duty. In many other cases, however, insubordination, imprisonment, and subsequent transfer to a lunatic asylum were more closely interrelated, with more adverse effects for the individual's life. Take the example of Daniel Bell, a 23-year-old gunner in the Madras artillery, who had attempted to stab his sergeant.[10] He was 'punished with solitary imprisonment', in consequence of which he became 'morose, suspicious, violent, and offensive in his language', so that admission to the lunatic asylum was considered to be indicated. Similarly, private William Wooley, a 24-year-old Englishman from Staffordshire, was on 13 April 1842

> pronounced to be of unsound mind by a Medical Board assembled at Trichinopoly in consequence of his having two days before, when a prisoner, attempted to strike a Sergeant with a steel fork, he having ordered him out for exercise when he was not inclined to go and after he had once refused.[11]

Officers who exhibited some aversion to carrying out their duty and failed to submit to superiors' orders were, in contrast to common soldiers, sometimes treated more leniently. A Lieutenant J.H. Hardisty of the Bengal native infantry, for example, was considered to suffer from 'weak intellect', as he had shown 'much disinclination for the performance of duty and invariably reported unwell when the regiment was ordered for exercise'.[12] The regimental surgeon saw himself therefore 'obliged to intimate to him that such a practice could not be permitted, and on his again absenting himself from parade without sufficient reason the Commanding Officer deemed it necessary to warn him of the consequences'. This official reprimand, 'together with the dislike to the performance of his duty' greatly affected Hardisty, yet did not prevent him from absenting himself again when 'directed to put the Regiment through part of its exercise'. Hardisty was finally to undergo examination by a medical committee. Although he did not manifest any mental symptoms and enjoyed very good general health, his refusal to attend to his duty as an officer made him 'totally unfit for the performance of duty'. Hardisty was pronounced 'imbecile' and sent to England 'to be placed under charge of his friends'.

It appears that for many the madhouse marked the endpoint of disciplinary measures. This is particularly true for the 'other ranks', as any deviancy from the norm of expected behaviour was seen as inexcuseable, deliberate and wilful disobedience and recalcitrance. Only when the usual range of disciplinary actions failed to have any desirable effect, or when measures such as solitary confinement occasioned the breakdown of prisoners' state of mental health, would punishment be substituted by treatment in the madhouse. Officers usually fared slightly better in that breaches of order and discipline on their part were met by the more 'temperate' responses seen to be due to persons of higher social standing. In some cases being pronounced 'insane' or 'imbecile' seems to even have been preferred to the verdict of a court martial, so that some allegedly 'mad' officers had in fact escaped the due process of the law by rendering themselves willing subjects of medical attention. Lieutenant Hardisty's case constitutes but one such example. The most blatantly obvious was that of J.D. Ouseley.

Ouseley, assistant magistrate and collector at Murshidabad, not only held a prestigious position in the Bengal civil service but also had the backing of his well-connected father, J.W.J. Ouseley, formerly in service in Bengal and subsequently lecturer in 'arabick' at the East India Company's College at Haileybury. When Ouseley junior therefore 'stabbed a Native' in October 1854, he was not to stand trial. His violent crime was considered to have been 'the result of temporary insanity',[13] which was believed to have arisen from 'too strict attention to his studies increased by his anxiety respecting an approaching examination'.[14] Ouseley was pronounced 'really insane and unfit to take his trial' in India.[15] He was sent back to England. On arrival he was delivered to his father's care 'perfectly restored to mental and bodily health'.[16] The well-known Haileybury professor petitioned Her Majesty and asked the authorities in Britain to take no further action against his son. He even solicited that his son be allowed to return to Bengal.

The necessary medical certificate was procured from the famous Sir Ranald Martin. It attested to the solely temporary character of young Ouseley's mental problems. Martin concluded after having carefully perused the several documents relating to the former lunatic's physical and mental state that 'he suffered much in health in India, from over mental exertion in office, and in the study of requirements for an examination at the same time'.[17] According to Martin he 'likewise suffered about this time from low fever; and while under both the influences . . . was subjected to severe solar exposure'. 'Under these disturbing causes', Martin held, 'the brain became congested and delirium was the result'.

Whitehall (and the Company) acquiesced to the plea. It was pointed out that as there was 'reasonable ground for supposing that the act of violence committed by Mr Ouseley was the result of temporary insanity, from which he has now recovered', it was not considered necessary to 'propose advising the Crown to take any proceedings against him in this country, and he will consequently be at liberty either to return to India, or to remain here unmolested according to his own discretion'.[18] In May 1857 Professor Ouseley was finally informed that permission had been obtained for his son to return to the East Indies.[19]

Though the madhouse frequently signified the nadir of the common sailor's or soldier's military career in the East, it did not necessarily mean the same to officers in the service. Being sent back home on medical certificate was certainly not perceived as the zenith of a lieutenant's or captain's professional life either, but in some cases at least it ensured that his career and reputation would not be adversely affected. In the case of an officer, disciplinary action after all may have entailed the withdrawal of commission – a situation dreaded by most as it implied not only the loss of a steady income but also a decline in social status (or, as Lieutenant Zouch put it when appealing to the members of the court martial, that a 'merciful construction' should be put on his action as otherwise his prospects might be 'totally ruined' and his 'character blasted and destroyed').[20]

The consequences of a certificate of unsoundness of mind seemed in contrast less drastic. Unlike common soldiers and sailors, officers could well be sent back on duty again when their furlough was over and any mental symptoms had vanished. It appears that their episode as mental patients did not necessarily expose them to any heavy adverse social stigma or occupational disadvantages. Lieutenant Zouch, for example, had after three and a half years furlough in England been back on duty in India despite his previous transformation into an artichoke. Ouseley, too, was permitted to again embark for India in pursuit of his career as a civil servant only three years after he had 'stabbed a Native'.

'Drawn very much from the same class'

Notwithstanding certain class-specific differences as to the social and occupational implications of medical certificates (and their occasional abuse), inmates of the three provinces' European lunatic asylums could in some respects be described as a relatively homogeneous group. Confinement in the madhouse was in many cases merely one step amongst several in a sequence of institutionalization. Inmates had simply been transferred from one institution to another: typically from the military barrack, to the hospital, back to the barracks, to the prison, to the asylum. Another important characteristic was that the bulk of European asylum patients (on average about 80 per cent) was made up of military servants. Out of the fifteen European patients confined in the Bombay Asylum in 1851/2, for example, eleven had previously worked as soldiers and sailors.[21] This fact tended to be a great equalizer. Most men were 'drawn very much from the same class, belonging generally to the same profession and united in a majority of instances by identity of interest, taste, and pursuits'.

But few civilians could be found in the European asylums in Madras, Bengal, and Bombay. In 1801 two out of seven Europeans in the Madras asylum were civilians, in 1808 the number of civilians reached four in contrast to twelve military servants.[22] Between 1841 and 1847 the Bengal asylum, for example, confined only eight civilian in contrast to ten times as many (eighty-three) military Europeans.[23] In part, this was simply because the number of non-military Europeans in British India was still low during the early part of the nineteenth century. Shortly after the Indian revolt, in 1861, only about 42,000 civilians as compared with about 84,000 military servants had taken up residence in the East.[24] Further, it was also true that an asylum frequented by public patients was not always regarded by relatives to be a suitable place of confinement for their dearest, however deranged. The very existence of Beardsmore's private lunatic asylum in Calcutta, for example (prior to his agreement with the Bengal government to receive public patients), owed much to the apparent need 'to accommodate female Patients and others wishing to avoid public Exposure of a family misfortune'. It also met the demand from those 'averse' to the idea of

> removing the relatives from their own immediate view to England where they have no connexions and to afford many other comforts, and conveniences which cannot be well expected or had at the public Hospital for Insanes.[25]

From what is known of the few European civilians who were admitted to one of the government-controlled asylums in Calcutta, Madras, and Bombay, it would indeed appear that in many instances these inmates did not have any family connections in India, or if so, their relatives were unable or unwilling to look after them at home.

Some civilian patients had suffered loss of some sort, either of fortune as in the case of a Captain J. Horne who endured a shipwreck in Penang in 1807, or of a close relative as was the case with many of the European women received into the madhouse.[26] Mrs Jonah Kiernan, for example, had come to India in 1835 with her husband James, formerly a labourer in Ireland, and then gunner in the East India Company's service.[27] The couple had three young children when James Kiernan died, in 1841. As a mere army-wife Mrs Kiernan had officially no choice but either to marry another man within the year and be allowed to stay on in India (as required by army regulations set up to deter European single women from permanently 'joining' a regiment and pursuing what were considered to be immoral and vicious activities), or else to be sent back home to a Britain, hit by what Hobsbawm has aptly labelled 'waves of desperation' in the shape of social pauperization.[28]

Mrs Kiernan, in fact, chose neither to re-marry nor to return to a life of misery in Ireland of which she was presumably glad to have seen the last just a decade earlier. From her husband's death onwards she had been 'in a distressed state of mind', and finally, on 1 January 1842, became 'so manifestly insane as to render it unsafe to leave her at large'.[29] She was first sent to the general hospital at Madras, and after a couple more months was transferred to the lunatic asylum in a generally 'taciturn and dejected' condition. Mrs Kiernan had meanwhile lost any 'interest in her children, to whom she previously appeared to be much attached'. The children, two boys and one girl, were consequently sent to the Military Orphan Asylum in Madras. This was possibly as much as their mother could have wished for them under the circumstances. Mrs Kiernan herself was sent to England where she remained in Pembroke House, supposedly suffering from 'dementia' until her death at the age of 78. According to the certifying doctor in Madras though 'generally appearing to understand what is said to her', she never uttered 'more than a single word in reply'. By remaining silent and permanently withdrawing into herself, Mrs Kiernan at least ensured that even in a situation as devoid of prospects for herself and her beloved children as the one in which she found herself in consequence of her husband's death, they would all be cared for somehow.

One of the central features of Mrs Kiernan's case (personal bereavement) was typical of other European women's life histories prior to confinement in the asylum. The previous history of male civilians was, in contrast, less homogeneous, although in their case, too, bereavement or loss of fortune were not uncommon events preceding institutionalization. Such gender-specificity certainly owes much to the relatively restricted range of activities open to European women in the East: mainly that of fulfilling the function of wife or mother. Failing that, they would at least be expected to live with their families, rather than pursuing any independent trade or profession.

The pattern of imprisonment – hospital admission – back to duty – imprisonment – hospital admission – transfer to lunatic asylum . . . etc. which so frequently characterized the personal history of military lunatics, was not typical of civilians. Rather, civilians' asylum admission was often (though of course not exclusively) a result of the *lack* (rather than the omnipresence) of a supportive social network, or of an institutional structure that could have assumed authority over the control of their behaviour, or responsibility for their care and security. However, the place where the ubiquitous web of colonial administration caught up with civilians was at the magistrate's court. There lunatics who had behaved in a disorderly fashion in public were taken by the police for certification. Those whose physical state appeared in the magistrate's opinion to be at least as badly affected as their mind, would of course initially be recommended for admission to the general, or police hospital for treatment and further observation. In many cases, however, certification at the court was followed by immediate reception into the lunatic asylum.

A passage from India

The European insane in India certainly possessed as a group several special characteristics which distinguished them both from the insane in Britain and from the Eurasian insane with whom they temporarily shared premises in India. Their predominantly military background and the practice of repatriation were largely responsible for this particularity. However, once Europeans were embarked for England, and finally arrived back home, the distinction seems to have blurred somewhat. First, it appears from the study of single cases that some amongst them recovered on their passage from India. (It is however just as impossible to ascertain their exact number as it is to judge whether recovery was attributable to madness having been feigned in the first place, or to the tendency of mental illness sometimes to subside spontaneously.)

Whatever the reason for such improvement, they would subsequently either be reunited with their families or, in the case of the poor, head for the streets, and sooner or later be picked up by the police and sent to the workhouse or back to the lunatic asylum. It was also not uncommon for lunatics to be simply disembarked by the ship's captain on arrival in the first English port, regardless of their state of mind. In most cases, however, the new arrivals would be received into a lunatic asylum: many of them into Pembroke House, and the rest into a military or naval lunatic asylum or one of many prestigious private madhouses. In these asylums, returned European lunatics would at long last find a fate similar to that shared by fellow-inmates in England's madhouses.

Few mentally ill Europeans with previous Indian experience (like the inmates of Britain's early nineteenth-century madhouses), would normally end up in the institution for ever – notwithstanding exceptions such as Mrs Kiernan. For one thing, the cost of maintenance in the asylum was high in England, and even higher in India. Europeans were therefore not only repatriated within a year, but would in many cases also remain in Pembroke House only until a relief of mental symptoms (rather than a perfect 'cure') occurred. The Company's authorities contributed towards the curtailment of the stay in the asylum by demanding, for example, regular returns from the proprietor of Pembroke House. In particular, the madhouse owner was obliged to assign reasons for every patient's confinement. This administrative control procedure did much to speed up discharges.

Further, the belief in the curability of madness was to decline only slowly during the course of the nineteenth century. Cures and relief of symptoms were therefore expected to occur, and comparatively high discharge rates were common. Although re-admission rates, too, were presumably high, confinement in an asylum did not as yet carry the threat of lifelong incarceration.

The slogan of 'no cure, no pay', spread by some private madhouse owners in England in order to attract clients, was certainly also instrumental in keeping the length of stay down. As did, in the case of Pembroke House, the fact that this privately owned establishment enjoyed the patronage of the East India Company. Such patronage seems to have been considered an obligation as much as a distinction. Dr. G. Rees, the owner who had in 1818 entered into the agreement with the Company to receive its insane employees, even advertised his establishment in the following way:

> The high encomium which has been paid to the management of This Establishment, in the latest investigation into the state of Mad Houses by the House of Commons*, and the distinguished patronage of the HON. EAST-INDIA COMPANY, render it unnecessary to say any thing more in its favor. It will be sufficient therefore to add, that the number is limited, the Patients are select, the

advantages are considerable, and the terms reasonable, and that *three-fourths of those already admitted have been restored to health and reason.*[30]

The place's suitability for members of the upper classes, and in particular for those with Indian experience, thus seems to have been unquestionable, and integrity of its proprietor's motives and his expertise in not only caring for the mentally ill but also achieving their cure, proven.

The changing fortunes of asylum inmates

Things changed however over the decades in Pembroke House and in the European asylums in India, as did their clientele. Patients' experience of asylum life would therefore not only vary greatly with their race and social position but also over time. Take the example of Mrs Nelson who was admitted to Beardsmore's asylum in 1827.[31] She was a Eurasian lacking any independent financial means. Her stay in the asylum was paid for by the Company and she was classified as a second-class patient. During the 1820s, 1830s, and even 1840s she enjoyed exceptionally good conditions, as the asylum proprietor was then still intent on attracting private patients who might be deterred if the place gained the reputation of a downmarket establishment. In the 1850s, however, when a government investigation found that the upkeep of poor lunatics attested to what was considered certain 'extravagance', Mrs Nelson's life was to change drastically. She was put on a parsimonious dietary regime and was in general provided for at an inferior standard. By that time the premises had also become overcrowded, and Mrs Nelson spent most of her time together with the many other women of mixed race, rather than with a majority of European women as she had done in previous decades.

In the first-class apartments institutional life was, of course, less obviously affected over the decades. G. Swinton, a military officer, for example, had been admitted to Beardsmore's asylum just two years before Mrs Nelson, in 1825.[32] Swinton, too, was born in India as the son of a European father and an Indian mother, and was therefore entitled to be sent to England for treatment. Yet on account of his officer status he was provided for as a first-class patient and was during lucid intervals even allowed to take his food at the asylum proprietor's family table.

Like other first-class inmates he was allocated his own separate apartment, which was equipped with hanging lamps, washing facilities and other objects for daily use. He also did not have to socialize with any of the thirteen ward-patients who then lived in less comfortable buildings in small and spartanly equipped cells.

Some three and a half decades later, at the age of 76 and suffering from 'dementia', Swinton was still an in-patient. About 1,200 European and Eurasian patients had by then passed through the asylum and the average asylum population had increased to about seventy inmates, only eight of whom were first-class patients. Swinton may then have missed the times when he was invited to dine at the proprietor's family table together with other gentlemen and ladies, as such practice was no longer encouraged once the place had become a public institution. The impact of changing times was however still much less on first-class patients such as Swinton than on the numerous second-class inmates who shared the ward with Mrs Nelson.

Being insane in British India

The question then arises of how the usual short-term and the, as yet less common, long-term confinement in the Company's asylums in India and in Pembroke House was perceived by inmates themselves. Only few and fragmentary accounts of patients' experience of asylum life exist, and those that are available convey more in regard to a patient's relationship with a particular medical officer than about the general impact of life inside the asylum on inmates' state of mind. Gunner Francis Harvey, for example, expressed his feeling of 'gratitude for the kindly interest' which he saw the superintendent to evince toward him.[33] Harvey's state of mind greatly improved under his medical patron's charge. Confinement in the Bombay asylum must on the whole have been experienced by him as a welcome relief from the harsh life in the military that had become so unbearable.

In a similar vein the medico who treated officer Thorne (who greatly disliked his father and mother, Colonel and Mrs Thorne of Baker Street, London) remarked that 'the most certain method of gaining his confidence is by treating him with respect'.[34] Lieutenant Zouch, the 'artichoke', too, seemed not at all ill-disposed to his confinement in the Bombay asylum. He was reported by his medical doctor to have taken pleasure in accompanying him 'regularly in a morning walk, taking great interest in the sea vessels and harbour'.[35] Zouch recovered considerably in the Bombay asylum, and, no further treatment in Pembroke House being indicated, enjoyed an extended furlough of three and a half years in England.

And, finally, even a man like gunner John Tremlett who was admitted to the Madras asylum as a second-class patient in 1842 (labouring under the delusion of being 'Marquis of Anglesca and Viceroy of India, sometimes a Highland chieftain' or 'Colonel of the 15th Hussare', and frequently complaining of 'not receiving the luxuries suitable to his supposed rank'), soon became 'more cheerful than formerly' and was 'easily controlled without personal restraint, and merely required a purgative occasionally'.[36] On transfer back to England he stayed in Pembroke House for about three months, and was subsequently allowed to live in '10 Horners Buildings', an almshouse in Southampton. From there he wrote to his former doctor at Pembroke House that he felt 'extremely obliged' to him for his 'care and attention'. (Tremlett went on to confide that he was 'sorry to say' that he had 'no prospect at present of any situation' and hopefully asked if the doctor could 'confer a favour' on him by recommending Tremlett for any prospective employment.)

Written evidence of patients' experience of life in asylums is particularly scarce in the case of those who belonged to the lower classes. This is even more so in regard to soldiers who suffered from a short spell of mental derangement, but were never admitted to the asylum. Yet the number of those who put on the sick list in their regiments on account of insanity appears to have been considerable. Some regimental health statistics reveal a high incidence of such short-term cases, but do not provide any further explanations as to the exact circumstances. What can be gleaned from the records is that temporarily insane soldiers were immediately on the relief of symptoms sent back on duty again. The overall number of military personnel afflicted by insanity may have reached about 4 per cent of all hospital admissions.[37] Only a very small percentage of these (between about 3 and 4 per cent) would however die from what was considered to have been mental illness.[38] This low mortality rate may have greatly contributed to the fact that regimental medical officers concentrated their efforts on recording the medical histories of patients suffering from the more fatal brand of diseases common among the soldiery in India rather than on the personal histories of patients who temporarily suffered from mental derangement.

One conclusion that can be drawn from the scarcity of patients' own accounts and of insufficient data on insanity in the barracks (and in the civil lines, for that matter), is that the story of the inmates of the three provinces' European lunatic asylums and of Pembroke House is only a partial and by no means a typical account of what it meant to be insane in British India. Further, and as pointed out by reformers and critics in more recent years who denounced institutional confinement as the incapacitation of the mad, the opinions, thoughts, and feelings of the very people for whom specialized institutions had been established, were in general (and apart from accounts of symptomatic behaviour) not considered medically relevant, nor important enough to be recorded in official documents. Only in few instances was patients' own evidence to be regarded as worth preserving. And even then it was usually by force of the intrinsic fascination of the story rather than because the narrative had been acknowledged on its own terms, that the material was saved from oblivion. The perspective from which 'mad tales from the Raj' can therefore be written is almost exclusively that of the Company's authorities and of the officers in the Indian medical service.

The general attitude that characterizes the situation was most aptly summarized by Dr W. Campbell of Bombay in 1852:

The Records of an Asylum, if rightly read are fitted to teach us many touching, and instructive lessons. They tell us of disappointed love, blighted hope, and crushed ambition, of exhausting labour, distracting care, and corroding sorrow, of time mis-spent, and precious opportunities lost, or misapplied; of unbridled passion, unresisted temptation; weakness, folly, dissipation, and crime.
With the lessons they inculcate, however, or the moral

they point, it is not our province to deal. We have to do rather with the causes, symptoms, and results of psychical disturbance and disease.[39]

To these latter we now turn.

5

Medical theory and practice

Popular images and medical concepts

Present-day images of the mad and of the treatment they could expect in previous centuries are frequently infused with stereotypes and sweeping generalizations. As has already been noted, there is the gloomy picture of friendless lunatics, exposed to squalid conditions, punishment, and neglect. On the other hand there exists the reverent picture of the mad as individuals endowed with supernatural capacities. As is the case with any stereotype, both images may contain a grain of truth. Augustan society for example tended to envisage, and frequently treated, the mad as bestial and sub-human, and the abominable conditions under which a James Norris was found to have vegetated for years in Bethlem Hospital does not entirely attest to the humanitarianism said to have characterized the Georgian age. Similarly, although the fabulous 'ship of fools' may owe its existence in great parts to poetic licence, the 'idiot colony' at Gheel was certainly no idle chimera.

Yet, neither the gloomy nor the sublime image does justice to the heterogeneity of social responses towards the allegedly abnormal in any epoch. Another flaw in these stereotypical images is that they tend to project the false idea of simple unilinear development. The history of the mad is construed as a development either from 'better' to 'worse', 'noble' to 'abominable' on the one hand or, from 'scandalous' to 'enlightened', 'dark' to 'light' on the other. Take the example of the picture Victorian reformers painted of Georgian attitudes towards the mentally ill. It reflects the conviction that the eighteenth century's dungeons had been replaced by well-

Figure 7 Naval Hospital, Madras, 1811. (Reproduced by permission of the Wellcome Institute for the History of Medicine.)

designed, clean, and airy establishments, that the miserable
state of institutions had been uncovered and rectified and that
the insane had been liberated from abuse, cruelty, and neglect.
In a similar vein, government officials and medical officers in
British India were convinced that they had imparted to India's
indigenous population a superior understanding of mental
illness that conceived of madness as a disease susceptible to
institutional treatment by experts trained in European
medicine.

It was also widely believed by the Victorian public in both
Britain and India that progress had been made in the scientific
understanding of insanity. And, indeed, the developments in
specialized institutional design, legal provision, and public
concern had been considerable. However, it seems that the
apparent progress owed much to the nineteenth-century
reformers' favourable evaluation of their own activities in
relation to that of their predecessors. Their propaganda has
obviously been quite durable, so that 'we still tend to view
eighteenth-century psychiatry through lenses polished by
nineteenth-century psychiatric reformers', and still tend to take
the contemporary characterization of early nineteenth-century
reformed asylum practice all too literally.[1] Concepts of insanity
in the first part of the century were immune neither to
social-political campaigns nor to practitioners' pragmatic
considerations. They did not qualitatively transcend late
eighteenth-century images, and they were neither derived from
nor constituted a single homogeneous body of knowledge.[2]

If we are to reject both the stereotypical images of barbaric
pre-Victorian conceptions of the mad and the romantic
glorification of earlier periods' allegedly benign approach to
the irrational, what then *did* characterize Georgian and
Victorian notions of mental illness? And to what extent were
concepts of madness among the British in India conditioned by
ideas in the colonial motherland?

During the Georgian period it came to be recognized that
the mentally deranged were not a species apart; that they were
not creatures without human qualities, but rather that madness
was the mental manifestation of a bodily disequilibrium that
could in principle affect anybody. Madness was not intrinsic to
a particular individual. Nor was it a feature that could be
explained in religious terms. It was the result of a false
connection of ideas. Mad persons 'err, as Men do, that argue

right from wrong Principles' was the ringing slogan of their period, coined by Locke.[3] This concept of madness as essentially *human* self-expression chimed in well with other predominant ideas in Enlightenment Britain. Benevolence and humanitarianism had become important ideologies, and the attitude towards special groups of society, such as children, women, slaves, 'savages', and in general 'the Other', softened somewhat.[4] This socially committed atmosphere inspired and nurtured ideas of social reform such as Robert Owen's 'new moral world'. It also stimulated that special branch of Scottish common-sense philosophy and social work that came into play fully in the early nineteenth century. Philosophically and ideologically the mad had become the target of social concern, paternalism and pity rather than objects of ridicule, persecution, or veneration.

Yet, the gulf between a permissive philosophical attitude and a do-gooder ideology on the one hand, and the way in which the mentally ill were actually treated by their fellow Georgians, was at times vast. Official reports on the abuse of the insane in some asylums and workhouses attest to this. Although the Victorians made a feature of such revelations as demonstrating their predecessors' unenlightened and inhumane attitudes and practices, their own practice did as often as not fail to heed the philosophers' words and the reformers' ambitions. Things were no different in British India.

The main lesson we can learn from such discrepancies is that wholesale generalizations about ideas and practices concerning the mentally ill in late eighteenth- and early nineteenth-century British India and Britain are inadmissible. Practice did not always follow on philosophy's heel. This was partly due to Georgian and (to a lesser extent) early Victorian individualism. Diversity of opinion was the order of the day – in British India as much as in Britain. Recourse was had not only to Locke's epistemology but also to Hobbes's and Pinel's writings as well as to those of Esquirol. Further, various other, traditional concepts of western medical thinking were integrated into these philosophical frameworks: the Hippocratic understanding of human life and disease in terms of body fluids, or humours; the conceptual framework of reflexes and neurological circles that developed out of the Cartesian tradition; Newtonian mechanistic models of nerve-fibre–behaviour interactions. The exercise of religious influence, too, was frequently perceived as an important curing aid.

As a consequence, logically incompatible categories were used eclectically by practitioners. Terminology was neither precise nor rigorously applied. What is more, the fact that doctors in India were not until the middle of the nineteenth century required to specialize in the treatment of the mad left many a doctor's basic knowledge of madness often no better than that of any informed layperson. It would therefore be an attempt doomed to failure to postulate anything like an 'authoritative definition' of *the* contemporary concept of insanity.

Nevertheless, those who dealt with the mentally ill (in Britain and in British India) shared some basic conceptual assumptions, and their various diagnostic and treatment patterns had some distinct features in common. To begin with, most doctors were influenced by a Lockean notion of insanity: that madpersons are essentially rational beings who reason rationally, but from false premises; that as all human beings affected by experience, they are not only fallible and prey to illusion but also amenable to re-education and moral guidance; that whilst the *insane* could be cured by manipulating their minds and treating their bodily afflictions, people who were described as '*idiots*' lacked reason and were therefore not amenable to treatment.

Other conceptual pillars of asylum management in British India were the regime of 'moral treatment' advocated by the Quaker Tukes who ran the famous York Retreat, and the dogma of 'non-restraint' implemented by Hill and Conolly during the 1830s and 1840s in English asylums. The language of 'moral therapy' and of the 'non-restraint' system certainly assumed centre-stage in official reports and regulations. However, these avant-garde and basically non-medical concepts constituted a certain professional challenge for the medically trained. The Tukes' understanding and treatment of the insane reflected their Quakerism, and Samuel Tuke's *Description of the Retreat* conveyed a humanitarian moral rather than any scientific medical analysis. Though usually devoid of such special religious background, asylum superintendents in India were still expected by the Company's authorities and the European public to share the Tukes' approach, and to implement what was considered to be the most enlightened treatment method of the times. Medical practitioners therefore were at pains to integrate a humanitarian perspective (that relied heavily on moral guidance and education) with their medical approach (which was in earlier decades mainly based on blood-letting, and later on pharmaceutical intervention). Not surprisingly, the result was a medley of at times contradictory treatment methods, and a tendency to pay lip-service only to 'moral therapy' and 'non-restraint'.

Medical laypersons such as the Tukes were not the only source for medical officers' official rhetoric. British physicians' medically oriented concepts of madness were being taken up, too, (although these would be less frequently referred to in official reports and government proceedings than the more accessible vocabulary of 'moral management'). John Brown's conception that virtually all diseases were due to an excess or deficiency of 'irritability', for example, had been influential in Britain from the late eighteenth century onwards, and also made its impact on European medicine in India until the early decades of the nineteenth century. The medical board of Bengal stated in a report of 1818 for example that madness was 'in nearly all its forms' a 'disease of great excitement, and high vascular action'.[5] Dr W. Campbell of Bombay even formulated the 'manifold objects' of his treatment method in reference to Dr Brown's ideas: patients should be supplied with occupations 'incompatible with unhealthy mental excitement'; their 'conditions of bodily health and comfort' should be secured; and 'the amount of restriction, as well as restraint' be diminished; whilst 'confidence, and protection and liberty' had to be increased; and 'painful impressions' be substituted by 'agreeable' ones. In short: the lunatic had to be brought 'into contact' with all that was 'pleasurable and pure and good', yet had to be shielded from exciting and irritating influences.[6] It is largely this Brunoian influence and its idea that 'great excitement' could best be diminished by depletive techniques, to which many asylum inmates (during the early decades of the nineteenth century) owed their debilitating treatment, and (in later years) assuagement of 'nervous irritability and restlessness' by means of narcotics.

Other reputed English physicians' ideas on madness were well received in British India. William Battie, for example, who 'pioneered clinical psychiatric teaching' at St Luke's in London had developed a relatively simple classification that combined both moral and somatic aspects.[7] Guided by his practical experience, Battie had come to differentiate incurable 'original madness' (congenital madness, idiocy, brain defects) from 'consequential madness' (the consequence of either physical or mental causes, characterized by deluded imagination and therefore curable). Seemingly clear-cut classifications like these were highly popular among Indian medical officers. In practice, however, they posed occasional problems, as admitted by the superintendent of the Bombay asylum as late as 1854. On attempting to argue an apparently recovered patient's case for immediate suspension from duty and transfer back home, he pointed out that it was at times difficult to 'draw a distinction between the higher classes of Imbeciles, and those who are nearly sane'.[8] Similarly, the decision whether an inmate was a 'maniac' or an 'idiot' was not always arrived at without problems, and sometimes led to squabbles among certifying doctors. A patient could suffer from 'mania' or 'melancholia' in the eyes of one practitioner and be labelled a 'perfect Idiot' by another.

Frequently attempts had been made to emphasize the differentiation of 'lunatics' or 'madpersons' (who might be violent, or at best incalculable in their behaviour) from mere 'idiots' and 'imbeciles' (who were considered harmless and manageable). Medical practitioners encouraged such differentiation as it enabled them to segregate patients and divert scarce institutional funds and staff attention to potentially dangerous or suicidal inmates. Although the mentally handicapped were considered to 'stand in need of more care than the needy, the aged, and infirm, the deformed and the diseased, who tho' feeble it may be in body, have yet sense and intelligence enough to minister to their wants', they could do with 'less constant and watchful supervision than the excited maniac or the desponding melancholic'.[9] Some government officials such as governor Falkland of Bombay favoured the distinction between 'alleged' lunatics (namely the 'imbecile', and 'idiots') and those who suffered from 'attacks of violence' and 'melancholia', in order to strengthen their argument for separate and less expensive institutions for the increasing number of the socially harmless among (Indian and Eurasian) asylum inmates.

It appears then that the categories of 'idiocy' and 'insanity' were difficult to handle as separate concepts – not only for members of the European public but also for many a medical officer lacking expertise in the treatment of the mentally ill and handicapped. Of census officials in the 1870s, for example, it was reported that the 'distinction between insane persons and idiots has not been understood by the enumerators', so that 'inmates of lunatic asylums have in many cases been returned under the latter title'.[10] Asylum superintendents, too, frequently used the terms 'idiot', 'maniac', and 'madman' interchangeably, or as vaguely descriptive of certain behaviour patterns rather than as precise conceptual entities.

Notwithstanding conceptual and terminological ambiguities, systems such as Battie's were in other respects very workable. Despite a seemingly psychological emphasis they could easily accommodate somatic concepts: the mind was clearly located in the brain, with both blood vessels and environmental and 'moral' factors exerting some influence, so that external stimuli such as blisters, leeches, douches, and cooling tonics as well as regulated diet and alcohol, purgatives and emetics, exercise and recreation contributed toward cure. Further, concepts such as Pinel's 'partial insanity' and Prichard's 'moral insanity' could still be used alongside the basic idiocy–madness delineation. Like the understanding that both 'moral' and 'intellectual' forms of insanity could be complicated by epilepsy and general paralysis, such systems were however seldom strictly applied in practice.

'Moral' therapy, 'mental' illness, and 'physical' derangement

It is well established that most early nineteenth-century classifications were based on a (in the last instance) somatic notion of mental illness – even when terms such as 'moral insanity' were used. The language of 'moral' therapy and management and the understanding that madness was caused by either 'physical' or 'moral' factors did perhaps much to mislead today's historians and psychiatrists who sometimes simply equate 'moral' with what is nowadays understood by 'psychological'.[11] Further, the talk of 'moral therapy' and 'moral causes' of insanity had a ring of ethical judgement about it. For example, lack of moderation was seen to cause certain forms of madness, and the 'superintendent's Moral Power over the Patients' was considered to be one of the central features of the proper management of the mentally ill.[12]

For the contemporary practitioner, however, these terms were not only applied in a less definitive way ('intemperance' for example could be referred to as either a 'moral' or a 'physical' cause of madness) but gained their meaning from a medical cosmology that fundamentally differed from present-day mainstream psychiatry, psychosomatic medicine, and clinical psychology. Factors which might today be considered as psychological causes – the death of relatives, exposure to unknown conditions, and anxiety – were then usually considered to be 'moral' in the sense that a particular event, state, or condition had a decisive impact on the whole person, affecting the whole system, and finally becoming localized in the brain, thereby giving rise to 'a disease called insanity'.[13] Given such basically *somatic* understanding of what came to be known as *mental* illness, the contemporary belief that many forms of insanity were (in theory if not in practice) amenable to cure by medicine just as easily as whooping cough, measles, and the like, was certainly not far-fetched.

Medical practitioners during the earlier decades of the nineteenth century did, however, not usually elaborate on the exact circumstances of their patients' cases. To them it was a clearly established fact that in India attacks of madness could 'in almost every instance be traced to exposure to the sun, hard living and other irregularities, exciting the action of the heart and blood vessels, and producing unusual determination to the head'.[14] The special circumstances of colonial life, and in particular of the military servant's life in barracks and camps was considered as unwholesome and characterized by 'peculiar temptations'. Service in the Company's army 'in the plains of India' tended to be evaluated as 'one unbroken course of physical degradation', bound to exert 'depressing influences on the mind and body'.[15] Factors such as unhygienic conditions as well as widespread abuse of the liquor bottle, sexual activities, loneliness, boredom, and 'constant observation of sickness, suffering, and death' were cited as the main reasons for many European regiments' disciplinary problems and their poor state of health.[16]

Although 'moral' factors appear to have had a peculiar precedence over 'physical' causes in exciting insanity, and despite numerous references to the importance of practising the enlightened and humane regime of 'moral' treatment, asylum doctors frequently attended merely to the diseases (such as cholera, dysentery, diarrhoea, fever, and syphilis), from which patients were seen to suffer in addition to, and independently of their insanity. In the Calcutta asylum, for example, the madhouse proprietors were supposed to guarantee that patients be treated with 'kindness and humanity'.[17] In this they appear to have failed, facing occasional criticism as to the absence of a 'more intimate and more cultivated experience of the varied forms and shades of mental diseases as well as a more enlarged philanthropy than appears to be . . . available in the Asylum'. The medical officer who was to be on duty for routine visitations and emergencies had only limited say in the asylum, and what is more, for twenty-seven years or so 'moral treatment' was reported by the medical board of Bengal to have been 'unaided and uncontrolled by the ordinary medical Attendant' who 'understood his duty mainly to consist in affording his advice and assistance to the bodily ailments of the Insane'. He would see a patient only on admission, discharge, or when something went wrong, but would not usually have any impact on his or her daily life in the institution. The situation was somewhat different in Bombay and Madras where the medical officer was at the same time the administrative superintendent. But even here, the medico usually restricted his activities to the more narrowly medical parts of his task, and left any day-to-day 'moral management' to his subordinates.

The impression therefore emerges that the concept of 'moral therapy' was somewhat of a 'white elephant' in British India: much talked about, but rarely seen. During most of the early nineteenth century medical officers mainly did what they had been trained for: they checked inmates' physical conditions, prescribed drugs in cases of acute restlessness, violence, and melancholic states, and carried out post-mortem examinations. Their approach was in practice narrowly medical. This became more apparent towards the middle of the century when the bodily basis of insanity, and consequently the precedence of medicine over management, was argued for in more explicit terms.

In that period the craze for phrenology and post-mortem investigations, and British doctors' attempts to counter laypersons' and moral therapy enthusiasts' continued transgression on what they considered to be their own exclusive sphere of expertise, reached the colony. W.A. Green, civil surgeon of Dacca, for example, pointed out in 1856 that insanity was 'essentially a physical derangement and alteration of the normal structure of the brain'.[18] He still mentioned Indians' 'noisy, and exciting, and exhausting' festivals and national ceremonies as well as 'indulgence in exciting and intoxicating drugs and liquors' as causative factors (alongside others such as 'visceral disease of the thorax and abdomen'). Yet, despite the admission of 'moral' causation, he considered insanity not to be 'a mere psychological disease, a merely strictly mental malady independent of physical change of the brain'.

In contrast to earlier theories the emphasis had shifted from vague postulation of blood vessels and brain activity as necessary intermediaries in madness, to the apparently clinically grounded belief that insanity was basically attributable to 'molecular alterations in the fibrous arrangement and tissue of the brain'.[19] Civil surgeon Green had during a period of six years cut open and dissected the skulls of seventy-six of his deceased asylum patients to pay homage to a medical approach which he claimed to share with doctors such as Forbes Winslow and J.C. Bucknill in England.

Green was not the only one who took an interest in his dead patients' brains, and his post-mortem findings were never unequivocally confirmed by other practitioners. The superintendent of the European and the 'native' lunatic asylum in Bengal, Dr T. Cantor, for example, too, spent a great deal of time and effort dissecting not only brains but also any other organs that could be taken apart. During 1856 and 1857 thirteen of his patients had died.[20] According to the asylum records, five of them had suffered from 'diseases of the nervous system' (hemiplegia, abscessus cerebri, apoplexy, exhaustion), another five from 'endemic diseases' (dysentery, diarrhoea, cholera), whilst two had died from 'old age' and one from 'caries'. Cantor was most anxious to provide as thorough a scientific analysis as possible. He made use of the microscope, drew up brief medical histories of his post-mortem subjects and left no organ untouched.

Unlike his colleague in Dacca, however, who had found 'morbid conditions of the brain' in all of his numerous corpses, and believed that 'insanity consists of, and is essentially a physical derangement and alteration of the normal structure of the brain', Cantor could not oblige with any such straightforward positive results.[21] Of those who had suffered diseases of the nervous system only three were 'attended with structural change of the brain'.[22] In the endemic cases only two 'presented cerebral, in addition to the ordinary phenomena', and in the remaining three cases, the former 'caries' patient's brain substance had softened, and one old inmate's lateral ventricles 'contained a quantity of serous effusion', while the remaining geriatric patient 'exhibited no cerebral morbid appearances'. And what is more, Cantor had to admit that because of the prevalence of various physical diseases supposedly alongside mental illness, it was difficult to differentiate the psychological impact of the one from the organic consequences of the other.

Apart from the general assumption that madness always had in the last instance an organic basis, both Green and Cantor fell short of drawing any more differentiated theoretical conclusions from the wealth of data they so meticulously gathered. In this they were typical of that brand of Victorian doctors who shredded a great number of their former patients, collated the resulting data in effusive tables, yet frequently failed to convincingly substantiate their conceptual statements with the evidence of concrete cases. At a period when the collection of artefacts, memorabilia, and objects *per se* was a widespread craze, statistics were by force of their factuality and richness of data perceived as a scientific end and accomplishment in themselves. Unaided by the authors, we are therefore left to rely on our own analytical aspirations if we wish to work out what the numerous tables of post-mortem data might tell us.

Nineteenth-century statistics in general are of questionable usefulness as reliable evidence of medical realities. They do however reveal the professional orientations and assumptions of medical officers. To nineteenth-century practitioners a multitude of raw data was a marker of the entry of methods and rationale of modern science into that sphere of medicine that had hitherto mainly been linked with speculation on the importance of lunar influences or with more practical concerns such as asylum design, 'moral management' and 'non-restraint'.

Green's and Cantor's clinical specialization and their obsession with post-mortems was not shared by every asylum doctor. Dr W. Campbell of the Bombay Asylum, for example, was a man with rather different professional inclinations who took greater interest in the stories his patients had to tell about their family life and work experiences. To Campbell, therefore, asylum inmates' previous history was more instrumental in elucidating the supposed mystery of their condition than was the scalpel. Yet, despite some variation in styles of management and medical specialization, images of insanity had in general begun to converge toward the middle of the nineteenth century.

It was of course not until the 1860s and 1870s that concepts of mental illness became more narrowly defined and the treatment of the mad administered in a more homogeneous way. Events such as the Indian revolt of 1857 and the change of guard from 'John Company' to the British Crown in 1858 were instrumental here, as was the British doctors Bucknill and Tuke's publication in 1858 of their eminent *Manual of Psychological Medicine*. Green's and Cantor's clinical emphasis can therefore be seen as foreshadowing a new medical paradigm in the treatment of the insane that emerged towards the second half of the nineteenth century.[23] More narrowly somatic concepts of insanity that tended to view the mentally ill as irrevocably mad were then in vogue. There was no more question that insanity was a 'disease' rather than an 'affliction', as had so frequently been argued (even by medicos) during previous decades. Bucknill pointedly expressed the belief that when a person was 'lunatic' he was 'lunatic to his finger ends',[24] and it was ideas such as these which were to quickly find favour with medical officers in India. Further, awareness of the high incidence of alcoholism, malnutrition, and infectious diseases, and the continuing accumulation of uncured patients inside institutions constituted the ideal breeding ground for assumptions of hereditary and organic factors and of racial predisposition to mental illness.

Above all, European colonial society as a whole had turned more race- and class-conscious, more hostile towards the indigenous population, and less permissive towards marginalized social groups. At a period when the spread of western education had enabled Indians to compete successfully for posts in the Indian Civil Service, the British could (as Ballhatchet pointed out in his work on *Race, Sex and Class under the Raj*) 'no longer assert their right to power on grounds of superior knowledge or intellect: instead they turned to arguments of racial superiority'.[25] Psychological models of 'impaired identity'[26] did not, of course, necessarily lend themselves to the discriminatory treatment of patients of different social and racial groups in lunatic asylums. They were however conducive to a colonial ideology that had begun to legitimize the colonial order of things by postulating certain races' and social classes' inability to gain the noble and indispensable characteristics that allegedly distinguished those men who then ruled British India.

Diagnostics and therapeutic practice

Despite the growing political and social importance of hereditary and narrowly medical concepts of madness and mental capacities, classificatory and diagnostic categories did not change to any great extent. The classic delineation of 'mania', 'melancholia', and 'dementia' was still as common in the 1850s as it had been during the 1800s. Dr Cantor, for example, included 'mania', 'dementia', 'idiocy', 'amentia', 'melancholia', 'monomania', and 'moral insanity' in his list of what he called 'forms of disease' (alongside categories less commonly used in asylum nosologies, such as 'phrenitis', 'hemiplegia', 'splentitis', and last but not least 'syphilis consecutiva').[27] This listing, though idiosyncratic and by no means exhaustive, contained the most distinct diagnostic categories then used in England and British India.

Other practitioners' classifications differed mainly in the extent to which they used subdivisions of the central disease categories. Dr Campbell, for example, not only differentiated 'dementia' from 'congenital idiotcy' [*sic*] but also split it up into two distinct entities: 'imbecility' and 'fatuity'.[28] The remaining categories he simply restricted to 'mania', 'melancholia' and 'monomania'. However much Cantor's and Campbell's schemes may be seen to differ in classificatory emphasis, they both still referred to a modified version of the same classical Greek system.

Yet the extent to which physical diseases (such as phthisis, epilepsy, scurvy, or syphilis) and insanity were assumed to be connected, varied. Dr Arbuckle, one of Campbell's predecessors in Bombay, for example, integrated into his nosological scheme conditions such as 'epilepsia', 'puerperal', and geriatric problems, and 'general paralysis'.[29] He however saw certain diseases as not so much inextricably linked with some forms of insanity, as manifest in addition to them. Arbuckle therefore used the descriptive categories of 'epilepsia and imbecility', 'epilepsia and mania', 'senile fatuity', 'general paralysis and idiocy', and 'puerperal mania'. Campbell in contrast classified the majority of patients as suffering simply from 'idiocy', 'imbecility', 'mania', 'melancholia', or 'chronic insanity'. In comparison with Arbuckle, then, Campbell's nosology differs slightly in conceptual outlook in that the latter concentrated on patients' mental affliction. Nevertheless, both perceived and treated the various physical diseases as mere 'complications' of insanity.

From today's point of view these kinds of classifications may well appear to have been based on quite diverse terminology if not different concepts. They would not conform to criteria such as those laid down in our day and age in the various versions of the famous (and infamous) *Diagnostic and Statistical Manual of Mental Disorders* (DSM) developed and marketed by the American Psychiatric Association, or the *Manual of the International Statistical Classification of Diseases, Injuries, and Causes of Death* (ICD), produced by the World Health Organization. Modern mainstream psychologists and psychiatrists who have been reared on the principle that any therapeutic measure ought to be based on sound diagnostics might, consequently, doubt the extent to which the treatment applied in the various asylums in nineteenth-century British India could have been efficacious. Contemporary practitioners were, in contrast, but little prey to the illusion that only allegedly clear-cut and sophisticated diagnostic labels could, if not guarantee, then at least be a requisite to cure or improvement of a patient's condition.

Men like Cantor used categories such as 'mania' and 'dementia' as descriptive rather than generic terms. 'Mania' basically was how a person behaved and appeared to another. It was the term used to describe the symptoms rather than the disease itself: the disease a patient suffered from was 'insanity', the way it manifested itself was through 'mania' or other 'forms of the disease'. Consequently, a patient might have been categorized as a 'maniac' at one time, and as 'imbecile' or suffering from 'moral insanity' at another. Not only would the diagnostic label vary with the patient's symptoms, but the treatment, too, would follow suit. Treatment was inherently geared towards what some of today's psychologists aspire to: a person-centred and flexible approach in diagnostics and therapy rather than a procedure that centres on psychological testing and screening. Unsatisfactory as symptom-based assessment and therapy may now be judged to be, it constituted in some instances an advantage to the patients. Inmates were, after all, responded to on the basis of the symptoms from which they were suffering at any one time, rather than in accordance with the diagnostic label stuck on them at an earlier assessment. Such an approach could at its best facilitate the establishment of an immediate and spontaneous therapeutic rapport and understanding between inmate and doctor. Some patients did in fact perceive the treatment that exclusively aimed at the relief of their symptoms as beneficial – even when they did not stand much chance of permanent cure. They were grateful for the doctor's attention to their mental problems and physical ailments, and appreciated attempts aimed at improving their well-being.

However, one has also to caution against any too enthusiastic an interpretation of what appears to have been an understanding and well-meaning method of person-centred therapy. On the basis of the little knowledge doctors had been able to accumulate on the aetiology of madness, they were not usually in a position to ameliorate the condition of those patients who suffered from mental problems brought on by infections, malnutrition, neurological diseases, or the like. The diagnosis 'mania', for example, could have been applied to capture the observable behavioural features that are associated with such different conditions as chorea (a neurological disease), syphilis, typhoid, malaria, 'reactive psychosis' (for example 'battle shock'), or even 'feigned madness' (in pursuit of furlough or discharge). Similarly, people can become paralysed or demented due to a multitude of very different factors, some of which require very specific medical or psychological intervention in order for treatment to be persistently effective. Hardly ever would the progress of conditions, such as paralysis, for example, be halted. Generally, therapeutic measures were applied on a basis of trial and error, and whilst in some cases this method proved most successful, it could be fatal, or at least ineffective, in others.

Aetiology and prognosis

Contemporary practitioners made some effort to discover their patients' previous history in order to determine the cause of their mental problems. The causes usually listed in case records ranged from more specific ones such as 'fear to be caught by a tiger', 'drunkenness', 'hereditary', and 'fall' or 'sudden fright' to vaguer terms such as 'vice' or 'exposure to unknown conditions and influence of tropical climate'.[30] However, apart from increasing a practitioner's knowledge (and arguably his understanding) of a patient's personal circumstances, awareness of events preceding mental derangement did not necessarily have any major influence on either diagnosis or treatment.

Prognosis, too, would usually be but marginally influenced by aetiological considerations. There existed, however, some exceptions. The 'weak-minded' or 'idiots' were expected to be beyond cure, although some improvement was occasionally admitted to occur. General paralysis of the insane, too, had been understood to warrant little hope, although the causal connection of this condition with syphilis had not been recognized. In the case of *Delirium Tremens* the situation was to a certain extent reversed. Here the causal link to alcohol abuse had been established. Reliable prognostic statements were, however, hard to come by. In general, doctors did possess some inkling about who among their patients would be likely to remain under medical care and in institutional custody for prolonged or intermittent periods. However, this knowledge stemmed more from longstanding practical medical experience and the continued observation of an individual patient's state of mind than from recognition of some specific feature in a patient's previous history.

If the connection between suspected causes, diagnosis, therapy, and prognosis was anything but clear, why then would doctors bother at all to find out about patients' personal and medical history? First of all, such investigation was formally required from early in the century by regulations devised in imitation of the recommendations by the metropolitan commissioners in lunacy in London, and motivated by the Company's desire to curtail public expenditure by tracing lunatics' solvent relatives. Then, by the middle of the century, it had become an ambition of many an asylum superintendent to not only attend to the mad but to provide some expert explanation of their protégés' mental problems. The nature of insanity was still surrounded by much 'mystery', and speculation about its origin was as rife among medicos as among the laity. By the 1850s asylum doctors found themselves having to provide medical reasons for unreasonable behaviour if they wanted to maintain their public and self-image as knowledgeable experts.

Most doctors in British India were further of the opinion that medical practice in the East had some unique features, and that certain physical and mental conditions tended to be different in appearance and intensity (if not in nature) from those experienced in more temperate climes. More thorough statistical documentation and detailed analysis was therefore considered to be a necessary step towards exploiting Company medicos' special 'position' in the East and 'its true value to science'.[31] The ambition of increasing the scientific knowledge of the aetiology of mental illness among Company servants was of course not shared by all asylum superintendents, and in many instances only lip-service was paid to the hospital boards' demand that a summary statement of the supposed causes should be provided in addition to more detailed information on each patient's previous history. The failure to provide such data cannot always be blamed on medicos' indifference or negligence, or their conviction that insight into the causes would be of minor relevance for their practical work. The wealth and detail of information made available to superintendents by the regimental doctors (who transferred patients from military stations to the European asylums) varied considerably and was, more often than not, decidedly sparse. Superintendents, on admission of new patients, therefore often had to rely on whatever information they could gather from hearsay – mainly from the attendants and invalid soldiers who had looked after the patients during their journey.

A further difficulty was that when information on patients' pre-history was available, it was not necessarily easy to determine what exactly may have caused a person's mental breakdown. Take the example of seaman Charles Curtis who was admitted to the asylum in Calcutta shortly after the Indian revolt of 1857/8.[32] Curtis had been suffering from syphilis and 'intermitting fever', and a history of alcohol abuse was suspected. He had also gone through the traumatic experience of service up-country during the 'Mutiny', leaving him in constant (and to a certain extent well-grounded) fear that he was 'going to be killed'. In this by no means rare case, the combination of various organic and psychological factors made any attempt to determine *the* cause of the patient's mental condition an inappropriate if not inadmissible endeavour.

There are many other cases that indicate that several factors could precede and, arguably, cause a patient's mental problems – even though doctors usually tried to focus on one or two of them. For example, several decades before Curtis, in 1820, a gentleman by the name of W. Phillips had been treated in the Madras lunatic asylum for then exactly two decades.[33] Phillips, who was considered to have led a 'chequered life', had formerly been a surgeon, then a captain in the Nizam of Hyderabad's service, and had also acted as 'a Player at the Theatre of Madras'. He had been received into the madhouse in 1800 on account of his 'extreme eccentricity of behaviour' and remained there until he was removed to England twenty years later. In the transfer papers Phillips's doctor mentioned that the patient had contracted syphilis a few years prior to admission to the Madras asylum. Nevertheless the doctor attributed the 'Mental Malady' to more general 'disappointments followed by habits of intemperance'.

It obviously was as tempting for Phillips's doctor in 1800 to point at one single suspected cause instead of acknowledging a complex interaction of a variety of factors as it might be for today's diagnosticians to lay their fingers on a possibly syphilitic origin. Whilst, however, today a valid diagnosis of 'lues zerebrospinalis' would occasion a treatment that might at least partially restore the afflicted patient's physical and mental health, Phillips's doctor did not possess the pharmacological means to do so, even had he determined syphilis to have been the presumed cause. The one thing the doctor was sure about was that 'there is not the smallest hope of this patient's recovery'.[34] (Phillips indeed was to remain an in-patient of Pembroke House near London for nearly thirty more years, before he died of old age.)

Treatment

If in cases such as that of Curtis, aetiological considerations had but minor impact on both the therapeutic process and prognosis, what then did the treatment consist of and what was the rationale behind its application? There is of course no straightforward answer to this question. Medical practice not only differed from practitioner to practitioner, but also changed during the course of the nineteenth century. In the earlier decades, for example, the use of mercury concoctions was widespread, as was the practice of bleeding patients. Yet these remedies were soon, mainly from the turn of the eighteenth century onwards, regarded as non-effective and even detrimental in a climate such as that of British India – and in particular in the case of insane Europeans. Purgatives and tonics, emetics and douches were then the main remedies adopted.

Phillips's fellow inmates in the Madras asylum of 1820 would, for example, seldom receive any other treatment than purgatives, leeches, and blisters, and even these would be applied in but few cases. It was considered effective enough to make patients take exercise, and to occasionally restrain them by means of the strait-waistcoat or to administer cold douches. In regard to Phillips it was said by his doctor that 'Medicines is rarely required', because 'exercise is freely taken' so that the patient's 'alvine evacuations' were regular. Restraint was imposed on him merely during the 'periods of the New and full Moon when he is apt to be noisy and abusive'.[35]

Towards the middle of the century, in contrast, doctors tended to supply more detailed information on what appears to have been a somewhat more diverse and versatile approach towards medical treatment. Take again the case of Charles Curtis. On admission to the general hospital Curtis was still suffering from an 'intermitting fever' which he had contracted during his service up-country.[36] He was also 'low spirited', and the certifying doctors established that Curtis had an ulcer on the penis. Curtis had arrived in hospital 'weak and anaemic', and remained in that state despite active treatment aimed at stimulating the body and counteracting physical weakness. He was put on a supportive regime of 'quinine and other tonic medicines', nitrate of silver lotion applied to the ulcer, and a nourishing diet of 'half mutton, with half a pound of extra bread and a pint of beer'. When necessary, 'occasional aperients' were prescribed in order to counteract any visceral sluggishness.

Curtis's treatment seemed appropriate not only for his poor physical state, but also for his steadily deteriorating mental condition. He was 'always in very melancholy mood', so that pharmaceutical measures that thwarted the 'nervous exhaustion' seen to be characteristic of melancholia were particularly indicated.[37] However, the medical regime did not effect the expected improvement. The hospital surgeons consequently entertained doubts as to whether the general hospital was the proper place for the patient. In particular as Curtis presented with 'delusions', hearing people 'continually talking about him', and being firmly convinced that 'he shall never be allowed to go out of the gate'. At the beginning his doctors had assumed that these mental symptoms were merely a consequence of the fever. Had he not a few nights after his arrival from the provinces been 'delirious and troublesome'? And had his mental condition then not been duly assessed as being 'periodic depending on the fever'? Yet, Curtis soon had 'delusions also between the paroxysms'. It was obviously difficult for the two doctors involved to make sense of the patient's mental symptoms, which were, so it appeared to them, unrelated either to the 'fever' or to the alleged syphilitic affliction. They had seen a number of patients suffering from alcohol-related problems, and on recognizing some symptoms as familiar they began to speculate whether Curtis had not previously had a history of intemperance. Yet, they were unable to 'find out that he ever was a hard drinker'.

Curtis's final transfer to the Calcutta madhouse in February 1860 seemed at the time the most opportune procedure. A madman in the hospital wards was not only irritating for other patients, but apparently also tended to stretch the hospital surgeons' expertise to the limit. Furthermore, it posed practical problems, as it was difficult to keep patients such as Curtis securely locked up. On one occasion, for example, Curtis had tried to squeeze himself through the window in his cell, and might have succeeded, had he not got stuck in a gap between the venetians and been found hanging in there 'as far as the waist'.[38] In the asylum, in contrast, Curtis would not be able to even get half-way out of the window. This institution was built to contain willing and less willing patients inside its walls and, unlike the general hospital, specialized in the application of various means of restraint. Furthermore, the medical regime then applied in the asylum by surgeon T. Cantor was geared towards restraining and quietening patients down. Dr Cantor was in favour of a highly regulated regime and regarded discipline, order, and strict surveillance of patients as an important pillar of modern asylum management techniques. He also emphasized the importance of medical experts' being in charge of the mentally ill, and considered medical prescriptions as the centre-piece of treatment. In place of tonic medicines Curtis was consequently made to take hyoscyamus, a drug that, depending on dosage, could be used as a narcotic or sedative.[39]

Medical treatment in the hospital certainly differed from that in the asylum. This discrepancy could however not simply be blamed on the hospital surgeons' lack of experience with insane patients. On the contrary, their specific remedies and their overall medical approach were well grounded in contemporary medical and emergent psychiatric theory. One of the features which differentiates the two approaches most, however, is the extent to which an attempt was made to not merely control the patient's mental condition by means of medical prescriptions, but to pharmacologically subdue him, and to discipline his behaviour in order to make him fit in with life in an ordered and regulated institution. This aspect of medical control over the patient is particularly prominent in Dr Cantor's administration of a sedative regime, and is all the more striking as Curtis had been described as 'quiet, but desponding, of few words and of melancholy expression of countenance'.[40] The patient therefore only constituted at most a minor threat to discipline, being by no means as troublesome to staff as those inmates who suffered from maniacal excitement.

Admittedly, Curtis's tendency to take to his heels for 'fear of being murdered' was annoying and unacceptable for asylum staff. Further, his treatment also included some tonic and rejuvenating measures such as 'exercise in the open air', cold baths, 'light reading' and 'light generous diet'.[41] Yet, it remains the case that even a harmless and withdrawn patient such as Curtis could be sedated. Unlike the strait-waistcoat which was used when need arose, Cantor's routine recourse to soothing prescriptions not only pre-empted the patient's attempts at escape, but also cut him off from the chance to experience the external world other than through a drug-induced haze. Asylum staff may well have found it easier to control and confine the patient; the profit gained by Curtis himself is however less clear, and he continued to be haunted by frightful images.

The pharmacological straitjacket was routinely used as a preventive instrument of institutional discipline by Cantor. It is perhaps not surprising that it is exactly the pharmacological approach, and in particular the use of sedatives and narcotics, which were to become increasingly prominent in the management of growing asylum populations in the second half of the nineteenth century. Cantor's regime is an early example of this tendency.

Although Curtis's case highlights the controlling aspect of medical treatment, Dr Cantor's preference for a sedative drug could of course not be seen as typical of *all* early nineteenth-century medical practice in India's lunatic asylums. Nor could the application of tonic medicines for a physically debilitated and mentally depressed patient such as Curtis be taken as representative of the treatment in general hospitals. Other medical officers in India may well instead have administered stimulant remedies or applied blisters to Curtis's head in order to substitute a real for an imaginary pain. Or they may have taken to these various different approaches in succession on a trial-and-error basis. Treatment patterns varied widely, not only from institution to institution but also with every medical officer.

The question of 'non-restraint'

There were certain areas of asylum management, however, in which relatively uniform adaptations were made to circumstances seen to be peculiar to a colonial situation. The question of what forms of restraint should be used in asylums was one that vexed all superintendents in British India considerably, especially as by the 1840s the doctrine of 'moral therapy' and of 'non-restraint' had in England become a must for those asylum doctors who wanted to consider themselves as advanced and humanitarian. Doctors in British India were consequently under pressure to follow suit, as the Company authorities and the parliamentary board of control expected them to implement what were considered to be the most enlightened regimes of the times.

Yet conditions in European asylums in India were (like those in many average institutions in Britain) not particularly conducive to what had by the middle of the century culminated in the demand for the 'total abolition of restraint'.[42] Insane patients, in particular the Europeans among them, frequently presented extremely violent behaviour, with unexpected attacks on attendants and fellow inmates, and sometimes almost continuous rages. Such 'maniacs' would towards the later decades of the century usually be doped with narcotics, whilst in earlier years attempts were made to weaken their vital energies by repeated use of purgatives and emetics. A debilitating regime could, however, not be sustained for prolonged periods. At a time, therefore, when the use of the pharmacological strait-waistcoat was not yet common, medical officers were not infrequently at a loss as to how to pacify those among their patients who constituted a threat to themselves, to others, and last but not least to asylum discipline.

According to the apostles of 'non-restraint' there existed only one alternative: 'classification – watchfulness – vigilant and unceasing attendance by day and by night – kindness, occupation, and attention to health, cleanliness, and comfort, and the total absence of every description of other occupation of the attendants'.[43] Dr Cantor of the Calcutta asylum echoed this view to a certain extent when he proclaimed that 'kindness is the real substitute for mechanical restraint'.[44] In addition to 'gentleness and watchfulness' attendants should be endowed with 'a certain tact, which, by abstaining from unnecessary interference, knows how to avoid aggravating excitement'. It was, however, exactly in regard to their staff's incapacity to adequately display such a characteristic that medical officers in India floundered. First of all, the low salary paid to European attendants was unlikely to attract employees amenable to the aims and ideals of 'moral therapy' and 'non-restraint'. What is more, there were but few positions available for Europeans, as Company officials were eager to cut down on staffing costs. The asylum in Bombay, for example, employed in 1852 only one European to look after up to fifteen European patients. Cantor had in 1857 only two – an apothecary and an overseer – on his books.

For the ordinary day-to-day management of the institution such scarcity of European attendants was compensated for by a greater number of Indian servants. In Bombay sixteen Indians belonged to the permanent staff, in addition to one ward attendant for every three European inmates (in contrast to one for every seven 'Natives'). Yet, when it came to dealing with violent European inmates, these Indian employees were considered of no use. There were several reasons for this. Medicos were convinced of the 'utter want of moral and physical courage of the native attendants'.[45] They also doubted whether an Indian could ever be expected to display that 'tact' that was necessary if they wanted to 'protect and control Insanes' without having recourse to mechanical restraint.

In the face of an insufficient number of European keepers, an alleged absence of integrity of character in Indians, and a notorious 'lack of means of proper seclusion and of padded rooms', superintendents could not help but admit that 'mechanical restraint could not with safety entirely be dispensed with'.[46] This view had been held from the early decades of the nineteenth century onwards. Although it was then couched in softer terms, the means used (such as coercion-chair, restraint-couch, manacles, and fetters) appeared harsher. By the 1850s the situation was reversed: the argument against 'total non-restraint' had become more insistent, and previously used instruments of restraint were 'consigned to the lumber-room'.

Although superintendents like Dr Cantor would concede that 'the system of non-restraint, in the ordinary acceptance of the term was established as the rule of the Asylum', straitjackets and thick fingerless leather gloves were still used – if only 'in cases of extreme violence', and whenever 'the malady intrinsically disqualifies Insanes'.[47] Examples of the latter case were instances in which patients were subject to 'secret vices'. In the more pernicious forms of this indelicate malady (which was also known as 'masturbational insanity') even straightforward remedies such as 'seton dorsi penis, vesicantia to the palms of the hands, and internal remedies' were according to Cantor known to fail, and, what is more, 'such vices [were] capable of eluding the strictest vigilance'. It was here that 'a pair of rigid fingerless gloves, joined together' and applied at bedtime had proved 'the only effectual remedy'.

The possibility of completely doing away with mechanical restraint had, however cautiously expressed, always been questioned. Even in Britain itself the discussion was more concerned with what sort of restraint was most acceptable rather than with its 'total abolition'. During the 1850s, however, a further dimension was added to the whole topic. Dr Cantor, for example, made it very clear that mechanical means were only second-best and only to be used 'till internal remedies allow the mechanical adjuncts to be discontinued'.[48] The pharmaceutical approach was to take precedence under usual circumstances. Only when medication failed, as in such exceptional cases as when 'during paroxysms of fury after the failure of soothing treatment, tonsure of the head, or application of vesicantia cannot be safely effected', was the temporary application of a strait-waistcoat, for example, considered legitimate.

Cantor summarized his advocacy of pharmaceutical and mechanical restraint with an argument which might in its essentials even be used by present-day practitioners objecting to critics' enthusiastic suggestions of reforms. In daily humdrum asylum practice medical officers were frequently, he argued, confronted with specific problems such as whether to apply ordinary fracture splints in order to 'protect some insanes against their propensity of inflicting sores on certain parts of the body'.[49] These however were mundane problems, which in Cantor's view 'those philanthropists who have carried the non-restraint system to its greatest perfection, have left subjects of speculation'.

The one argument that was considered most compelling in the advocacy of mechanical restraint was that of patients' resistance to coercion by physical force. Doctors Laycock and Noble were cited by Cantor as well-known practitioners in Europe who held mechanical appliances 'preferable to a struggle between Patient and Attendant'.[50] The observation of several of Cantor's predecessors in the three European asylums in India also indicated that 'mechanical appliances cause[d] less excitement than physical force'. Cantor adapted this point to Indian conditions when he talked of 'a peculiar condition well deserving of notice' and characteristic of the treatment in India of European lunatics, namely 'the sense of humiliation or degradation which certain classes, Soldiers and Sailors in particular, are in the habit of attaching to coercion by the hands of native Attendants'. Cantor claimed to recall instances 'in which convalescents who distinctly remembered the paroxysm, have expressed gratification at having escaped the "shame of being laid hands upon by natives" '.

This was strong language, but one that befitted a topic that touched upon the disturbing possibility of physical encounters between Europeans and Indians. After all, Cantor produced his reflections on 'non-restraint' in May 1858, when the Indian revolt (characteristically labeled the 'Mutiny'), which had not quite succeeded in forcing British rule in northern India to its knees, was not yet completely quelled. What then shocked the European community at large was akin to what upset the superintendent's and his patients' minds: the nagging idea and obnoxious reality that Europeans were being vanquished by native colonials.

In the event Cantor himself provided what he called a 'remarkable illustration' of Europeans' and in particular of military servants' dread to be 'laid hands upon by natives'.[51] A field officer, 'distinguished no less by his services than by his gentlemanly qualities' had gone mad while on leave in another colony. He had been locked up in a jail, and subjected to bodily restraint. On arrival in the Calcutta asylum 'his expression was wild, and he was inclined to become violent', so that Cantor asked the obvious question: 'Should he not be locked up and coerced by natives?'. A clear and unhesitantly expressed answer followed: 'Certainly not'. It went without saying that this officer was not only a European but undoubtedly also a gentleman. No wonder then that his 'word not to escape was sufficient'. The patient recovered, following a 'successful course of treatment', and revealed during Cantor's first visitation that the 'appeal to his honor . . . had effectually subdued him'. Moreover, it was the 'freedom from mechanical restraint, and of all things, from being coerced by natives' that had made 'a deep impression upon him'.

The gentleman slumbering in this patient had obviously conquered the madman's maniacal inclinations. In the case of this officer the suspicion that early nineteenth-century 'moral therapists' and 'non-restraint' advocates succeeded in replacing external coercion by internal restraint, manacles and physical force by psychological pressure, is certainly confirmed. The patient's inclination to stick to his word may have been motivated as much by the ambition to live up to what was expected from a gentleman as by the unsettling thought of having to undergo the humiliation of physical restraint by those whom he would under ordinary circumstances never let come near him. Yet, the aim and result were the same: the patient was not to be coerced by Indians. It was for the representatives of British rule to mete out blows, and not for its vassals.

Social discrimination, racial prejudice, and medical concepts

Racial prejudice was certainly omnipresent in British India – inside institutions as much as in the community at large. So

were considerations of social precedence. These were expressed
not only in a system of classification of inmates that foremost
implied segregation according to social class. The language
used to describe European gentlemen's and gentlewomen's
mental condition, too, was less harsh and seldom even vaguely
derogatory as it was so often in the case of lower-class soldiers
and pauper patients. The gentlemanly yet violent officer under
Dr Cantor's care was merely referred to as a man whose
'intellect had been affected', just like the gentleman fifty years
before him, who had suffered loss of fortune and reason
simultaneously, had been considered to have been affected by
temporary 'weakness'. Lower-class patients would in contrast be
talked of as 'perfect Idiots' and 'maniacs'. This is not to say that
diagnostic categories such as 'mania' or 'dementia' were not
applied in the case of first-class patients. However, they would
rarely be mentioned in case reports and official correspondence
other than by euphemistic expressions. Some practitioners, like
surgeon J. Callagan of the Madras medical board, even went as
far as disapproving of 'dooming' gentlemen 'to the humiliating
scenes of a madhouse' where they would have 'nothing before
them but the distracting gestures and clamours of Maniacs of all
Countries and of the lowest Ranks in life'.[52]

Social discrimination was not only confined to the expatriate
community, being characteristic also of Indian society. Nor was
it altogether unheard of among Georgians and Victorians in the
colonial motherland. Widespread as discrimination may have
been among the various peoples in Europe and India, examples
of British snobbery certainly highlight the extent to which racial
and social exclusiveness influenced medical perceptions and
impinged even on areas of such marginal socio-political
importance as lunacy provision.

Ubiquitous social discrimination and its colonial pendant,
racial prejudice, were of course also highly instrumental in the
formation of judgemental ideas on the comparative incidence
and nature of mental illness among the various social classes
and races in British India. In fact, apart from the question of
restraint, racial and social sentiments were more prominent in
no other area of asylum medicine than in the epidemiological
discussions of the 1850s. Views on the spread of mental illness
in British India had of course been greatly nurtured by
conceptual developments in Europe. In Britain Dr J. Reid
expressed in 1808 the commonly held view that 'Madness

strides like a Collossus in the country'.[53] One explanation was that the perceived steady increase in the incidence of insanity could largely be accounted for by the progress of civilization. The more people were exposed to modern ideas and ways of life, and the more educated they became, the more susceptible would they be to mental derangement. People who lived in remote and secluded areas (such as the Welsh mountains and the Scottish highlands, or in the allegedly less developed parts of southern Europe), were in contrast considered to be not only simple and contented but also psychologically more stable. Susceptibility to mental derangement was the price a nation had to pay for its spiritual and economic progress.

Matters were, however, less straightforward in British India. Whereas during the earlier decades British doctors here, too, were convinced that madness was less widespread among simple village folk and unsophisticated Indian town dwellers, they had to employ considerable mental acrobatics to uphold this argument by the middle of the nineteenth century. Assumptions of inherent racial inferiority had become particularly pronounced in India at a time when western education had been propagated by liberal reformers as the 'panacea for the regeneration of India'.[54] Once that Indian, but English-educated middle class, a 'class of persons Indian in colour and blood, but English in tastes, in opinions, in morals, and in intellect' had been raised (and had been ready to compete with the British for positions in trade and administration), the liberal vision of India's regeneration had turned sour. Consequently the view gained prominence that by virtue of education alone an Indian could never be civilized enough to become a legitimate candidate for government positions (or, for that matter, for insanity!).

By the time of the 'Mutiny' at the latest it was widely believed that an Indian would intrinsically never be able to rise above what was considered to be the inferior characteristics of his race. Was it not a fact that Indians were naturally endowed with inferior mental capacity? Was not their mind possessed of a 'feeble texture' that could easily become unhinged? Such considerations were, of course, not easily compatible with the position that allegedly uncivilized people were less prone to mental problems, especially as it was simultaneously held by many Britons that Indian culture possessed some strangely irritating aspects. Indian festivals and national ceremonies, for example, were almost always described as noisy, exciting and exhausting, and therefore of a kind to 'frequently upset the mind'.[55] It was further believed that Indians were prone to 'indulgence in exciting and intoxicating drugs and liquors'. From the point of view of a British expatriate such alleged cultural idiosyncrasies could not but be interpreted as a 'rife cause of insanity in the feeble minds of the poorer Asiatics'.

Such diversity of racial and cultural preconceptions tended to produce a range of conflicting and contradictory statements on the comparative spread and incidence of insanity in British India. Civil surgeon W.A. Green of Dacca, for example, argued within a few lines of the very same article in the *Indian Annals of Medical Science* in 1857 that the 'occurrence of insanity amongst the natives of India and the East is probably as frequent, if not more so, than in the temperate and colder climates of other parts of the world', and that the 'mind of the Bengallee and Hindoostanee is not assailable in so many points as that of the lower orders of European countries'.[56] Instead of stressing the hackneyed contemporary argument that the European lower classes' tendency to succumb to vice and liquor was due to a lack of willpower, Green operated from a racial perspective: compared with Indians, lower-class Europeans' 'intelligence and range and grasp of apprehension (and consequent obnoxousness [*sic*] to so many more stimulating and deranging influences)' were 'so much greater'. To complicate the argument even more, Green went on to point out that 'the very poorer order in other countries' were 'numerically less insane than the same class in the East'. This particular phenomenon he attributed to the alleged fact that 'the feeble texture of the mind of the later class' would 'more readily' give way 'before the disturbing causes' – although he made the reservation that these cases were 'fewer far than those by which the minds of a more generally enlightened people are liable to be disconcerted'.

Muddled and logically incomprehensible though this analysis by Green may appear, it contained the main strains of thought then widely held by both medical experts and laity. In a more blunt fashion these had been consolidated to the position that however much

> natives of this country suffer in comparison to Europeans as regards their intellectual endowments and perceptions, they are so far gainers in being considerably less disposed

to become the subjects of disease implicating that delicate and highly-organized structure, the brain and its appendages, the functions and physiology of which are so little understood, but which are seen to be more or less susceptible of derangement as we advance or descend in the scene of civilization.[57]

A somewhat more differentiated and unusual, albeit still racially biased, view was maintained by Calcutta-based surgeon J. Macpherson, and published in the *Calcutta Review* in 1856. Macpherson held that insanity was not, contrary to common belief, more prevalent in civilized countries, but simply assumed a different form and was taken more notice of than among the 'ignorant', 'uneducated', and 'superstitious' of countries such as India.[58] He also criticized other 'popular views' on this topic such as those advanced by Copland, Prichard, and Oesterlen in Britain. Macpherson shared their belief that 'southern nations are less subject to insanity than northern ones', yet refuted the position that 'Europeans going to the Tropics are especially liable to attacks of the nervous system', and labelled accounts such as that of Europeans' physical and mental debilitation in the East being reminiscent of the 'fabled "Armida's Garden" of Ariosto' as pictures 'too highly colored' and drawn 'only from the accounts of travellers'.

Although Macpherson's argumentation went against some of the essentials of contemporary mainstream medical thought, his report on 'Insanity among Europeans in Bengal' was frequently referred to by colleagues. He was one of few asylum superintendents who had attempted to prove their general point by means of statistical data (even though Macpherson himself admitted to having underestimated the incidence of madness to a significant extent, and regimental returns like those published in 1855 on the 1st Bombay European Regiment showed that 'affections of the mind form a large item' in the statistics on invalids, namely 14 per cent).[59]

East is East, and West is best

Reflections such as those of Macpherson, and to a lesser extent of Green, were part of the more general debate on whether Europeans could ever become acclimatized to conditions in the East. This debate was not only a harbinger of medical ideas about degenerationism which became so influential during the second half of the nineteenth century, but was also of great socio-political importance, as signalled by the provocative title of an article by assistant surgeon A.S. Thomson, published in the *Transactions of the Medical and Physical Society, Bombay* in 1843: 'Could the Natives of a temperate climate colonize and increase in a tropical country and vice versa?'[60] The question of whether white settlers should be allowed to set up home in British India had always been controversial. One main argument in favour of white colonization implied that 'our Indian possessions' would be rendered 'more secure' – although this view was easily shattered by those who pointed out the lingering danger of settlers 'throwing off the yoke of the mother country' (as had happened in the case of the Spanish and Portuguese in South America and, even closer to the heart of the British, in consequence of the American War of Independence).[61]

In the realm of medicine the question was tackled in a not less controversial way. The central concern here was whether European settlers could 'live and produce pure offspring in India'.[62] It was feared that they were 'likely to become degenerate' within a few generations – 'from the climate and connexion with low ignorant women'. The evidence close at hand was open to diverse interpretation, though. People of Dutch and Portuguese descent, for example, were considered 'both mentally and physically degenerate'. Their case was taken as a good illustration of 'the injurious effect of climate on the descendants of Europeans in India'. It was however conceded that 'their constitutions are rendered more adapted to the climate by a union with the aboriginal inhabitants'.[63] Nevertheless, was it not the unequivocal experience of many a British mother that her children frequently suffered debilitating illnesses and did not thrive easily in India's plains? Was it not with difficulty that European children were 'brought to maturity' and that soldiers in European regiments were kept alive and good-humoured without the privilege of sick-leave to England, which was such a vital factor in the preservation of the health of higher-class civil servants and officers? 'There is little doubt', concluded Dr Thomson of the 14th Light Dragoons, 'the tropical parts of the world are not suited by nature for the settlement of the natives of the temperate zone', and if the children of the British were not sent back to Europe they would become 'stunted in growth and debilitated in mind'.[64]

Contrary to the theory of 'acclimatization' (then prominent among doctors in Britain, and which concluded that even the British could eventually habituate themselves to the alien Indian climate), most expatriates tended to agree with Thomson. The Indian climate was believed to be inhospitable and dangerous. It got on the skins and nerves of those who were reared under a less fiercely burning sun, under the gentle tepid drizzle of maritime conditions. The enduring 'solar myth' emerged, of the power of 'heat and dust' to set off a whole range of nagging and unsalubrious ailments and impediments, from prickly heat to insubordination, from heat-stroke to adultery and manslaughter, depression and paralysis, nervous exhaustion, irritability and neurasthenia. Victorians of course set out to take control of as many aspects of life under the Eastern sun as possible and took measures to ameliorate its detrimental effects: civilians' office hours implied an early rise and a long break during midday; the military started its troop marches and physical training before sunrise; and only mad-dogs and few Englishmen were found outside bungalow or barrack without one of the specially designed 'topees'.

Yet, it was not only the Indian climate in its narrowly meteorological sense that upset Europeans. It was the whole range of social and cultural trappings peculiar to their life in the East. The attitude of the majority of British expatriates had with every decade of the nineteenth century become increasingly hardened in its hostility towards their Indian environment. This was seen to abound in hidden dangers, to be host to uncivilized and barbaric (yet intriguing and fascinating) practices, and to have a dire effect on the unwary European. Perhaps one of the more poignant expressions of this is the insistence by most medical officers on European lunatics' early removal from India. Medicos held that although 'it affords good ground . . . for a recommendation that [a patient] should not return to duty', it 'must be admitted, that in no instance, after an attack of insanity should a man be permitted to remain in circumstances and relations which are obviously so likely to lead to a relapse'.[65] Even the hills that were so agreeably cool and relatively isolated from the madding Indian crowd of the plains, were no alternative to the green and pleasant lands of home.

The practice of providing European lunatics with a passage to England owed its instant appeal to the European community's endeavour to permanently dispose of embarrassing members of the white ruling class, as much as to medical considerations of the healing power of repatriation. The deportation policy however also fitted in well with the contemporary mainstream image of the nature of British colonialism in India. The British hold of its 'Indian possessions' was usually considered to be a lasting engagement, culminating during the heyday of the British Raj in an 'illusion of permanence'. At the same time there existed strong doubts as to the extent to which a place like India could ever become permanent home to the British. The majority of British expatriates considered themselves basically as transients who took up the highly lauded burden of the white man, and would eventually, in health or sickness, sanity or madness, be shipped back to 'Blighty'. There was no better cure for an ailing and alien Company servant than 'home'. This view was not only cherished by most Europeans in British India. It was shared by great parts of the medical profession and became the hallmark and centre-piece of the treatment of those afflicted with insanity.

Medical authorities in British India drew heavily on the concepts and treatment methods prevalent in the colonial motherland. At the same time these principles were refracted through the distorting prism of the colony's severe climatic conditions and its peculiar racial and social ideology. A special, colonial brand of medical theory and practice emerged: British in origin, but adapted to the requirements and morals of a local community of expatriates.

6

'Mad dogs and Englishmen . . .'

In the preface to his famous *Folie et Déraison* Michel Foucault asserts

> Faire l'histoire de la folie, voudra . . . dire: faire une étude structurale de l'ensemble historique – notions institutions, mesures juridiques et policières, concepts scientifiques – qui tient captive une folie dont l'état sauvage ne peut jamais être restitué en lui-même.[1]

No such total analysis in the structuralist sense has been intended here. Nevertheless, the aim has been to reconstruct the history of European madness during 'John Company's' time as completely as surviving sources allow. The treatment of the European mentally ill has consequently been analysed in relation to colonial ideology, state policy and legislation; the important role of public opinion 'at home' in Britain and in the colony in the construction of treatment methods and administrative control measures has been highlighted; and the reconcilability of commercial interests, colonial ideology, and humanitarian motives has been discussed.

Further, the comparatively early and successful intervention by the colonial state in the 'lunacy sector' has been related to the persistent endeavour of Company officials and of the expatriate community more generally to preserve the image of the European elite as a clique of formidable and impeccable colonial rulers. Institutional arrangements in the three main asylums were revealed as determined by the same colonial ideology – notwithstanding local specificities and contingent events. The institutions incorporated and reflected the values and practical concern of colonial society at large: the *idée fixe* of

Figure 8 The New General Hospital, Calcutta, 1829. (Reproduced by permission of the Wellcome Institute for the History of Medicine.)

social precedence, and the concomitant snobbery; the extension of class barriers into racial prejudice and aloofness; and an insistence on racial and social segregation that during the course of the nineteenth century increasingly widened the gulf between the British ruling elite, its lower-class compatriots, and the Eurasian and Indian communities – inside as much as outside the madhouse.

The policy of sending the European insane back to Britain served as a particularly poignant reminder that the Company took swift measures to make 'invisible' those who might otherwise tarnish the image and self-perception of the British as a mentally and physically superior people. Despite relative numerical insignificance, the institutionalization and repatriation of the European mentally ill retained a symbolical importance that went far beyond its proximate function of controlling socially harmful and embarrassing individuals and 'subjugating unreason'.

Furthermore, the madhouse became one of the markers of socio-economic and scientific progress and of the allegedly superior qualities of western civilization. The rise of medical practitioners to social status and professional recognition helped to advance the case of western medicine towards the middle of the nineteenth century. Although it was conceded that 'the study of Insanity' was a 'branch of medical education utterly ignored by the licensing bodies' and that there were 'few in the public service who can be supposed to know any thing about it',[2] medical doctors became decisive promulgators of the enduring colonial myth of western medicine as an excuse if not legitimation for colonial rule.

For those made 'invisible' by means of institutionalization and deportation, and at the receiving end of medical and psychological intervention, confinement did not necessarily constitute an unwelcome assault on their mental and bodily integrity. Patients belonging to all classes of society as often as not preferred treatment in the institutions to the harsh and challenging life in military barracks and civil stations. Despite gradually deteriorating provision and discrimination against lower-class inmates, the lunatic asylums in British India turned only slowly from refuges or temporary receptacles to 'total institutions'.

Medical paradigms as well as treatment methods varied considerably and were by and large derived from the imperial motherland. Restricted and vague as they were in scope and explanatory value, they evolved in harmony with the special environmental, ideological, and social demands of the wider colonial context: the tropical climate necessitated less drastic medication and a modification of architectural principles; tribute was paid to racial superiority and social snobbery by substituting the doctrine of 'total non-restraint' with the advocacy of occasional mechanical restraint; medical reasons were repeatedly advanced against the view that Indians could ever be raised above their allegedly inferior mental and physical 'nature'; and the equally taxing assumption that Europeans could gradually 'acclimatize' themselves to life in the tropics without becoming mentally and physically degenerate themselves was rejected.

Despite the attempt to provide as complete as possible a picture of 'European madness in colonialism', many questions still remain unanswered. For example, what about the assumption that people with different regional origins, temperament, and historical and religious backgrounds may have experienced life in the Company's army and navy in distinctly different ways? A bag as mixed as that of the English, the Welsh, the Scots, and the Irish – not to mention recruits from various countries on the Continent – did not always respond to the call of duty in that unison demanded by the regulations and promulgated by the authorities. There is in fact much evidence in patients' case reports that communication problems between the various national groups and quarrels about religion and national idiosyncracies were not only implicated in soldiers' and sailors' psychological breakdown but were as common a feature of social life in the army and navy as was the maliciousness and brutality of some non-commissioned officers and the disregard for recruits' feelings of self-esteem and personal integrity so characteristic of the military.

Yet because of the multitude of factors (or overdetermination) that usually go along with the development of mental problems, it is difficult to single out 'regional origin' as a distinctive and discrete cause of emotional breakdown or madness. Despite this caveat, the prevalence of nationalism and of feelings of 'regional identity' must be taken as one factor of importance in Company employees' history of mental illness, if not as a relevant aspect of military life in British India. This may be an uncomfortable speculation as it runs against the grain of one of the enduring myths of empire: the alleged existence of an unshaken and unshakeable 'esprit de corps' (and the identification of each individual with the cause of colonial rule often seen to go along with it). A deeper analysis of patients' life stories and of institutional histories would be required to further substantiate these speculations.

A further query that may arise from an overall assessment of the evidence advanced, touches upon the question of whether the 'social control' aspect of emerging psychiatry was in fact not much weaker than commonly suggested. If it is true that somatic diseases, malnutrition, and alcoholism accounted for the majority of deaths and hospital admissions; that hospitalization in the asylum on account of mental illness was a comparatively rare occurrence; and that emotional breakdown and mental problems were, in the military, dealt with first of all by punishment or temporary furloughs, whilst among civilians they were seen to fall within the purview of the police, then the case for 'social control' may indeed appear negligible. Another presupposition may then need re-assessment on similar grounds: that of increased 'medicalization' or of the process by which ever more personal ailments and areas of social life become subject to medical attention and control.

The notions of 'social control' and 'medicalization' are in fact easily overdone – as is that of any other concept if the impression is maintained that a phenomenon as complex as that of madness in colonial rule could easily be explained by a few catch-words. There was more to it than the 'control of the rabble' and the advance of medicine or the 'subjugation of unreason' by the discourse of reason and science. The most relevant of those other factors have been touched upon in the foregoing analysis. Yet far from resigning ourselves to the resolution that our subject is too complex and difficult to allow for definite judgements, we may still legitimately conclude that the confinement of the mentally ill, and, more so, European medicine (and emergent psychiatry) were eminently instrumental in the maintenance and legitimation of the colonial endeavour. It is however not so important what institution-alization, repatriation, and the work of European medicos achieved on a *practical* level. Performance in this respect was as a matter of fact quite restricted during most of the nineteenth century. The central point is consequently not that of medicine as an effective 'tool of empire', but that of the persistent *myth* of medicine as a tool of and excuse for colonialism. It is here, at the point where medicine was, and still is, considered as a cogent reason for colonization that we need to reconsider the talk of social control, of the all-embracing nature of medicine, and òf the tools of empire.

And finally, it may be noted that not much has been said about the impact on westerners of India as a culture. Does it not appear right to assume that the variety of cultural heritages of India would have left a strong impression (not to say occasional confusion) on Europeans' minds? Was it not the case that the British conceived of themselves as strangers in an alien place? What then about any perceived 'Indianness' of the ailments that affected Europeans in India? Exposure to unfamiliar cultures is after all nowadays conceived of as a psychological stressor and as a possible factor in the development of behavioural and mental problems. The possibility of 'culture shock' appears the more legitimate since in fact contemporaries themselves conceded, and occasionally warned, that life in the tropics would leave its mark on Europeans' physical and mental health.

There are however several reasons why this question is difficult to answer. First of all, nineteenth-century medical practitioners and scholars *did* attest a crucial role to the Indian environment – yet the way in which India's 'alien sky' was conceived to impact on westerners, differed fundamentally from today's conception. Where we would nowadays talk of an alien environment in terms of 'culture', 'customs', and 'beliefs', contemporaries would elaborate on the 'climate' (in particular on heat and cold, atmospheric pressure, marsh effluvia), on the quality of the water, and on geographic features. Early nineteenth-century medical thought was still very much akin to the Hippocratic corpus of *Airs, Waters, Places*, and the prevalence in far-away countries of environmental conditions so different from those of the British Isles did much to revive this classical body of thought. Further, the process of colonial penetration itself widened the scope for environmental theories by enabling westerners to come into contact with peoples of hitherto scarcely known lands, and to speculate on how the various living habitats had formed their 'character', and might influence the well-being of European traders, soldiers, and civil servants raised under more temperate conditions.

The first half of the nineteenth century was of course also the period of 'moral management', of 'moral insanity' and of the understanding that 'moral' as well as 'physical' factors could lead to madness. Yet the connection between morals and insanity was by no means prejudicial to the environmental paradigm. Both Hippocratic theory and moral managers conceived of madness as squarely and ultimately located within a somatic framework. What is more, although the talk of 'moral management' and 'moral causes' was widespread, the theory did not take off in practice to the extent it had in some model institutions in Britain. Ill-health in the tropics was thus by and large linked to exposure to the heat of the sun, to high humidity and the emanations from the earth. Even the age-old connection between lunar constellation and nervous irritability found new esteem.

It is to a large extent this conception of a person's well-being in terms of bodily functions and environmental and moral influences which makes it difficult for a modern observer to determine whether 'culture' as we conceive of it today was seen as – or was in reality – a relevant factor in the causation of mental derangement. This problem is further exacerbated by the fact that preventive and curative medicine relied heavily on physical intervention and manipulation. Environmental influences were quantifiable and therefore open to correction by means of the introduction of certain ascertainable standards: a carefully measured amount of food and drink, of space or air per person in barracks, hospitals, and asylums; a clearly circumscribed set of times of daily outdoor exercise, and regular shower baths and ablutions; restricted contact to the outside world; and routine transfer to the air and place of long-term patients' native land. These were the important determinants (though not guarantees) of a healthy institutional life in the tropics. Not surprisingly, then, 'culture' appears even in the more elaborate of case reports on asylum patients usually as a mere (unquantifiable and therefore irrelevant) background factor and at best as part of an unhealthy basic environment.

The possibility of 'cultural alienation' as a factor in Europeans' mental derangement is further obscured by the fact that the British aimed at *avoiding* contact with the culture of their subjects. In extension of the barrier of social class that was so characteristic of late Georgian and Victorian society in Britain, the ruling elite in India kept itself aloof from Indians and imposed restrictions on the extent to which its lower-class compatriots were allowed to interact with the indigenous population. 'Going native' became increasingly disapproved of over the decades. It was seen as the doubtful virtue reserved for a few eccentrics or irrecoverably 'Indianized' Brits of otherwise impeccable social standing (such as Sir Charles Metcalfe, a distinguished Company official, whose political achievements and local knowledge were appreciated, although his extensive Indian family was rarely publicly referred to).

The ordinary soldier and sailor would have but few occasions to socialize with Indians, and was therefore by and large spared estrangement by unfamiliar sights and customs. Marriage quotas were restricted and, although in the nineteenth century the number of Indian camp-followers was considerable, with porters, water-carriers, horse-grooms, bacon-*wallahs,* prostitutes, and the like roaming the vicinity of camps in their hundreds, they were kept at bay and out of bounds during most of the day by watchful serjeants. Segregation was less easily enforced at sea ports where hawkers, beggars, harlots, and hands hired by the hour would hover around East Indiamen moored in the harbour. Yet, here, too, the 'native' parts of towns were no-go areas. The contact that did occur between men of the west and people of the east was largely that between Indians who offered their services and Europeans who made use of them – a constellation that was bound to create that combination of racial and sexual dominance, assumed superiority, and petty-oppression (rather than induce feelings of cultural alienation) that is typical of interpersonal relationships in colonial situations.

Nineteenth-century British colonialism is particularly renowned for its peculiar transplantation of class barriers and its distaste for social intercourse with its colonial subjects. It is perhaps not surprising then, that at a period when private cross-cultural contacts were disapproved of and restricted by force of regulation, the majority of Europeans would rarely have a chance to go 'doolally' on account of encounters with Indian 'culture'. Although the authorities warned that observation of Indian rituals and ceremonies might unhinge the Indian's and European's mind, and 'often revealed anxiety at the thought of British soldiers wandering beyond the controlled environment of the cantonment into mysterious places where they might be infected with dangerous diseases and tempted into Oriental vices',[3] it was the climatic conditions of India or an 'exposure to unknown conditions' that were suspected by asylum super-intendents as causes of madness.

A further dimension is added to the question of cultural causation by the high incidence of disease, malnutrition, alcoholism, and death on account of cholera, fevers, liver problems, diarrhoea, and dysentery. Any speculation about singular causation in the onset of insanity therefore appears ill-conceived. It may well be that people were likely to die from some physical disease before they even had a chance to develop any adequate mental symptoms.

Finally, it should not be forgotten that most Europeans in British India belonged to the military or navy. Within these institutions mental and emotional problems became conspicuous primarily on account of their behavioural consequences. Although madness was considered to be a disease amenable to treatment by medical experts, any deviation from the norm of disciplined and ordered behaviour was at first interpreted as insubordination, and consequently routinely dealt with by disciplinary means. What military authorities were concerned with was primarily a correction of the undesirable behaviour rather than the alleviation of personal suffering. There was not much room here for considerations about subordinates' personal problems and difficulties in coping with the demands of military life. It was the language of 'disgraceful and highly irregular conduct and neglect of duty to the prejudice of good order and discipline' that was heard in barracks and mess decks, not the talk of emotional breakdown, nostalgia, or cultural alienation. Even in those few cases in which transfer to the lunatic asylum occurred, medical certificates echoed the discourse of discipline and order. The reputed 'burden' the white man had to bear in the east was to a large extent that of his own culture: the burden of restrictive British institutions, of parochial social communities, and of the malice and vindictiveness of superiors and comrades.

Nevertheless, it remains somewhat misleading to graft today's interest in 'culture' onto nineteenth-century socio-political realities and medical cosmologies. The more so as what really is at stake is the economic, social, and psychological impact of colonial rule. The concern with 'culture shock' and 'cultural alienation' is then more likely to distract from the far more pertinent topic of colonial penetration. Modern theories on cultural influences by and large conceive of different cultures as independent realities and rarely take into account that it is the relationship between social groups that conditions the scope and limits of contact between their cultures. In regard to colonial history this means the relation of rulers to the ruled. Balandier emphasized this point when he asserted that it was myopic to investigate the contact between 'cultures' in isolation from the contact between racial groups and in disregard of the socio-political reality of colonial groups.[4] One of the main aims of this study has certainly been to locate 'madness' in its wider socio-political context and to elucidate further the profound effect colonialism had not only on Indians but also on the dominant as well as on the subordinate group of the European community. In that sense the intention has been to provide a critical account of 'madness in colonialism' that goes beyond both Balandier's partisanship for a politically inclined scientific analysis and one of the popular images of the Raj as a place where only 'Mad dogs and Englishmen go out in the mid-day sun'.

Primary sources

Official archives in the India Office Library and Records, London

Despatches from London

Civil Judicial Despatches to Bengal (Lower Provinces)
Commercial Despatches to Bengal
Financial Despatches to India
Judicial Despatches to Bengal
Legislative Despatches to Madras
Legislative Despatches to India
Military Despatches to Bengal
Military Despatches to Bombay
Military Despatches to India
Military Despatches to Madras
Political Despatches to India
Public Despatches to Bengal
Public Despatches to Bombay
Public Despatches to India
Public Despatches to Madras
Public Works Despatches to India

Letters (despatches) to London

Judicial Letters received from Madras
Legislative Letters received from India
Military Letters received from Bengal

Primary sources

Military Letters received from Bombay
Military Letters received from India
Military Letters received from Madras
Public Letters received from Bengal
Public Letters received from Bombay
Public Letters received from India
Public Letters received from Madras

Government proceedings/consultations

Bengal (Lower Provinces) Civil Judicial Proceedings
Madras Judicial Proceedings
Madras Legislative Proceedings
India Legislative Proceedings
Proceedings of the Legislative Council of India
Bengal Military Proceedings
Bombay Military Proceedings
India Military Proceedings
Madras Military Proceedings
Bengal Public Proceedings
Bombay Public Proceedings
India Public Proceedings
Madras Public Proceedings
Bombay Public Works Proceedings

India Office files/selected material

Board's Collections
Court's Minutes
Miscellaneous Letters, received
Miscellaneous Judicial Letters, received and sent
The Records of Pembroke House and Ealing Lunatic Asylum,
1818–92
Revenue, Judicial, and Legislative References

Private papers/demi-official correspondence

India Office Library and Records: MSS

Richard Compton
John Luck
A Grenadier's Diary

Primary sources

Centre of South Asian Studies, Cambridge

Mrs Montgomery's Letters

Official publications, governmental reports/commissions

The British Library, London

Report from the Select Committee on the state of criminal and pauper lunatics and the laws relating thereto, 1807
Reports from the Select Committee on the better regulation of madhouses in England, July 1815, April–June 1816
Reports of the Metropolitan Commissioners in Lunacy
Hansard's Parliamentary Debates
Parliamentary Papers, House of Commons
Parliamentary Papers, House of Lords
Census of the Island of Bombay (Bombay: Education Society Press, 1864)
Memorandum on the Census of British India of 1871–72 (London: Eyre and Spottiswoode, 1875)

Wellcome Institute for the History of Medicine Library, London

Royal Commission on the Sanitary State of the Army in India (London: Eyre and Spottiswoode for HMSO, 1863) 2 vols.

Notes

Ex oriente lux – the light of the Orient

1. E. Stokes, *The English Utilitarians and India* (Delhi: Oxford University Press, 1982 [1959]), p. XI.
2. E. Eden, *Up the Country* (London and Dublin: Curzon, 1978 [1866]), p. 70.
3. S.C. Ghosh, *The Social Condition of the British Community in Bengal, 1757–1800* (Leiden: Brill, 1970), p. 73.
4. C. Allen, *Plain Tales from the Raj. Images of British India in the Twentieth Century* (London: Macdonald Futura, 1981 [1975]), p. 19.
5. Maud Diver, 1909, quoted in Allen, *Plain Tales*, p. 57.
6. P. Spear, *The Nabobs. A Study of the Social Life of the English in eighteenth century India* (London and Dublin: Curzon, 1980 [1932, 1963]), p. 126.
7. C.A. Moore, 1953, quoted in V. Skultans, *English Madness. Ideas on Insanity, 1580–1890* (London: Routledge & Kegan Paul, 1979), p. 33.
8. Eden, *Up the Country*, p. 77; Horace Walpole, quoted in Skultans, *English Madness*, p. 27.
9. Moore, writing on Abbé le Blanc, quoted in Skultans, *English Madness*, p. 33.
10. P. Woodruff, *The Men who ruled India* (London: Jonathan Cape, 1971 [1953]), vol. 1, p. 380.
11. Spear, *The Nabobs*, p. 148.
12. F. Fanon, *Peau noire, masques blancs* (Paris: Editions du Seuil, 1952). F. Kramer, *Verkehrte Welten. Zur imaginären Ethnographie des 19. Jahrhunderts* (Frankfurt am Main: Syndikat, 1977). M. Leiris, *Die eigene und die fremde Kultur* (Frankfurt am Main: Syndikat, 1979). P. Rack, *Race, Culture, and Mental Disorder* (London and New York: Tavistock, 1982).
13. See for example Woodruff, *Men who ruled India*, p. 180.
14. See for examples notes by E. Thompson, in Eden, *Up the Country*, pp. 397–8.
15. Woodruff, *Men who ruled India*, p. 180.
16. *'My Dear Mother . . . if for ever o a due, sell not my ole close'. Gunner*

177

John Luck's letters from India, 1839–1844 (London: India Office Library and Records, manuscripts), introduction.

17. Eden, *Up the Country.*

18. *Letters from Richard Compton, 1856–1858* (London: India Office Library and Records, manuscripts), 22-6-1857.

19. Md Mil Proc, 23-3-1821.

20. T. Williamson, *The East-India Vade-Mecum* (London: Black, Parry & Kingsbury, 1810), vol. 2, p. 320.

21. M. Foucault, *Folie et Déraison. Histoire de la folie à l'âge classique* (Paris: Librairie Plon, 1961), p. VII. (le 'morose état civil de[s] prisons').

22. Ghosh, *Social Condition,* p. 1.

23. Spear, *Nabobs,* p. 6.

24. Ghosh, *Social Condition,* p. 99; Spear, *Nabobs,* p. 10.

25. Ghosh, *Social Condition,* p. 74.

26. Spear, *Nabobs,* p. 22.

27. I. Munro, quoted in Ghosh, *Social Condition,* p. 70.

28. Ghosh, *Social Condition,* pp. 65, 70.

29. Spear, *Nabobs,* p. 26.

30. K.K. Dyson, *A Various Universe: A Study of the Journals and Memoirs of British Men and Women in the Indian Subcontinent, 1765–1856* (Delhi: Oxford University Press, 1978), pp. 154, 155.

31. F.G. Hutchins, *The Illusion of Permanence. British Imperialism in India* (Princeton: Princeton University Press, 1967).

32. V.G. Kiernan, *The Lords of Human Kind. European Attitudes to the Outside World in the Imperial Age* (Harmondsworth: Penguin, 1972 [1969]), p. 37.

33. Spear, *Nabobs,* p. 137.

34. Spear, *Nabobs,* p. 140.

35. E.J. Hobsbawm, *Industry and Empire. From 1750 to the Present Day* (Harmondsworth: Penguin, 1981 [1968]), p. 88.

36. Resident at Indore to I Govt, 31-10-1838.

37. Spear, *Nabobs,* p. 140.

38. Anon. *Observations on India,* 1853, quoted in Spear, *Nabobs,* p. 141.

39. Charles Grant, quoted in A.T. Embree, *Charles Grant and British Rule in India* (London: Allen and Unwin, 1962), p. 169.

40. Royal Commission on the Sanitary State of the Army in India (London: Eyre and Spottiswoode for HMSO, 1863), p. XXIV.

41. Spear, *Nabobs,* p. 63.

42. Ghosh, *Social Condition,* p. 89.

43. Stokes, *Utilitarians,* pp. XII, XIII.

1 Madness and the politics of colonial rule

1. P. Spear, *The Nabobs. A Study of the Social Life of the English in eighteenth century India* (London and Dublin: Curzon, 1980 [1932, 1963]), p. 70.

2. Bm Minute, 7-9-1850.

3. Separate Minute, Bombay, 7-12-1850.

4. P. Spear, *The Oxford History of Modern India, 1740–1975* (Delhi: Oxford University Press, 1984 [1965]), p. 65.

5. Spear, *Nabobs*, p. 79.

6. P. Woodruff, *The Men who ruled India* (London: Jonathan Cape, 1971 [1953]), vol. 1, p. 153.

7. Mill, quoted in E. Stokes, *The English Utilitarians and India* (Delhi: Oxford University Press, 1982 [1959]), p. 48.

8. Mill, quoted in Stokes, *English Utilitarians*, p. 48f.

9. Stokes, *English Utilitarians*, p. 51.

10. Carlyle, quoted in Stokes, *English Utilitarians*, p. 50.

11. Bm Minute, 13-7-1820.
    Bm Med B to Govt, 3-7-1820.
    Bm Med B to Govt, 3-8-1820.

12. Bm Med B to Govt, 3-7-1820.
    Bm Med B to Govt, 19-6 -1820.

13. Bm Med B to Govt, 3-7-1820.
    Bm Med B to Govt, 19-6-1820.
    G.O. Bombay, 4-9-1827.
    Quarter Master Gen to C-i-C, Bombay, 8-8-1826.
    Bm Asylum Report, 31-3-1852.

14. Bm Med B to Govt, 24-8-1850.
    Bm Pub L, 16-4-1851.
    Suptd Surgeon Karachi to Commissioner in Scinde, 1-2-1850.
    Bm Minute, 22-3-1850.
    Commissioner in Scinde to Govt, 12-9-1850.
    Bm Minute, 14-10-1850.
    Govt Bm to Govt India, 29-11-1853.

15. Bm Med B to Govt, 22-6-1852.

16. India Pub D, 9-11-1853.

17. A.T. Embree, *Charles Grant and British Rule in India* (London: Allen and Unwin, 1962), p. 169.

18. Chief Mag Calcutta Police to Govt, 30-1-1840.

19. Bg Pub L, 21-7-1818.

20. Spear, *Oxford History*, p. 210.

21. D. MacDonald, *Surgeons Twoe and a Barber. Being some Account of the Life and Work of the Indian Medical Service (1600–1947)* (London: Heinemann, 1950), pp. 108, 134.
Minute by Lord Dalhousie, 14-6-1852.

22. Resolution, Md Govt, 13-12-1808.

23. Bm Med B to Govt, 18-3-1801.

24. Bg Hosp B to Govt, 4-2-1788.

25. Stokes, *English Utilitarians*, p. 34.

26. V. Skultans, *English Madness. Ideas on Insanity, 1580–1890* (London: Routledge & Kegan Paul, 1979), p. 111.

27. Skultans, *English Madness*, p. 112.

28. Skultans, *English Madness*, p. 109.

29. Beardsmore to Bg Med B, 2-5-1836.

30. A. Halliday, *A General View of the Present State of Lunatics, and*

Lunatic Asylums, in Great Britain and Ireland, and in some other Kingdoms (London: Underwood, 1827), p. 65.

31. Bg Pub D, 5-2-1851.
32. Bg Med B to Govt, 21-2-1818.
33. Bg Govt to Med B, 17-3-1818.
34. Bg Med B to Govt, 10-3-1851.

Historical evidence of abuse can be read either as evidence of the relative inadequacy of the system (as suggested here), or as evidence that the system worked quite well in that it did indeed discover and act upon such abuses. Additional evidence which shows that nothing effective was done about revealed problems, and that the same problems recurred in the same institutions, is needed to discriminate between these two possible hypotheses. See for such evidence: W. Ernst 'The Establishment of "Native Lunatic Asylums" in early nineteenth-century British India', in G.J. Meulenbeld and D. Wujastyk (eds) *Studies on Indian Medical History* (Groningen: Egbert Forsten, 1987).

35. Bg Mil D, 26-8-1818.
36. Stokes, *English Utilitarians*, p. 10.
37. Spear, *Nabobs*, p. 55.
38. Bg Mil D, 8-4-1816.
39. Stokes, *English Utilitarians*, p. 60.
40. Stokes, *English Utilitarians*, p. 35.
41. Stokes, *English Utilitarians*, p. 46.
42. Stokes, *English Utilitarians*, p. 35.
43. Grant, quoted in Stokes, *English Utilitarians*, p. 34.
44. India Pub D, 17-4-1857.
45. *Royal Commission on the Sanitary State of the Army in India* (London: Eyre and Spottiswoode for HMSO, 1863), p. XVII.
46. *Royal Commission*, p. XIX.
mortality (all causes, 1814–1833) soldiers: 69 in 1000; officers: 38 in 1000.
47. Bg Med B to Govt, 26-8-1835.
48. India Pub D, 18-9-1839.
49. Chief Mag Calcutta Police to Govt, 30-1-1840.
50. India Pub D, 1-12-1852.
51. Bg Comm D, 13-3-1833.
52. Md Citizens to Govt, 28-11-1851.
53. Minute by Govr Falkland, Bombay, 7-9-1850.
54. Note by Sec to Bg Govt, 9-6-1852.
55. G.A. Berwick, MD to Bg Govt, 5-3-1847.
    Bg Med B to Govt, 20-10-1847.
56. Bg Asy Report, 31-3-1852.
57. J. Macpherson, 'Report on Insanity among Europeans in Bengal, founded on the experience of the Calcutta Lunatic Asylum', review in *Calcutta Review*, **26**, 1856, p. 607.
58. Minute by Govr Falkland, Bombay, 7-9-1850.
59. Act XXXVI of 1858, Section 4.
60. Act IV of 1849 was modelled on: 39 & 40 Geo III, c. 94; 1 & 2 Vic, c. 14; 3 & 4 Vic, c. 54.

Acts XXXIV, XXXV, XXXVI of 1858 were modelled on: 16 & 17 Vict, c. 70, 96, 97.

Act 14 & 15 Vict, c. 81 integrated: 39 & 40 Geo III, c. 94.

61. *A Grenadier's Diary*, 1842–1856 (London: India Office Library and Records, manuscripts).

62. Minute by I.E. Drinkwater Bethune, Leg C of India, 10-6-1848. Minute by Bethune, Leg C of India, 30-6-1848.

63. Minute by I.E. Drinkwater Bethune, Leg C of India, 10-6-1848. Minute by Bethune, Leg C of India, 30-6-1848.

64. Minute by Lord Dalhousie, Leg C of India, 16-6-1848.

65. Minute by I.E. Drinkwater Bethune, Leg C of India, 10-6-1848. Minute by Bethune, Leg C of India, 30-6-1848. Minute by Lord Dalhousie, Leg C of India, 16-6-1848.

66. Minute by Lord Dalhousie, Leg C of India, 16-6-1848.

67. See also W.Ll. Parry-Jones, *The Trade in Lunacy. A study of private madhouses in England in the eighteenth and nineteenth centuries* (London: Routledge & Kegan Paul, 1972), pp. 64–70.

68. Macpherson, *Report on Insanity*, p. 596.

69. Minute by Govr Falkland, Bombay, 7-9-1850.

70. Table shewing the number of public patients treated in the Lunatic Asylum at Bhowanipore, and the results from 1 January 1824 to 30 December 1850.
Bm Asy Report, 31-3-1852.

2 The institutions

1. W. Ernst, *Psychiatry and Colonialism: The Treatment of European Lunatics in British India, 1800–1858* (University of London, School of Oriental and African Studies: unpublished PhD thesis, 1986).

2. *Records of Pembroke House and Ealing Lunatic Asylum, 1818–1892* (London: India Office Library and Records), Medical Certificates, Case Books.

3. W. Ernst, 'The Establishment of "Native Lunatic Asylums" in early nineteenth-century British India', in G.J. Meulenbeld, D. Wujastyk, (eds), *Studies on Indian Medical History* (Groningen: Egbert Forsten, 1987), p. 198.

4. J. MacPherson, 'Report on Insanity among Europeans in Bengal, founded on the experience of the Calcutta Lunatic Asylum', review in *Calcutta Review*, **26**, 1856, p. 595f.

5. Minute Govr Falkland, Bombay, 7-9-1850.

6. *Census of the Island of Bombay* (Bombay: Education Society Press, 1864), p. II.

7. *Memorandum on the Census of British India of 1871–72* (London: Eyre and Spottiswoode, 1875), p. 37.

8. Bg Med B to Govt, 27-3-1851.

9. MacPherson, *Report on Insanity. Royal Commission on the Sanitary State of the Army in India* (London: Eyre & Spottiswoode for HMSO, 1863), vol. 1, p. 592. Bg Med B to Govt, 20-10-1847.

10. W. Ernst, 'A Case of Intellectual Insanity', in *History of*

Psychiatry, 1 (2), 1990, pp. 207–22.

11. MacPherson, *Report on Insanity,* p. 603.

12. MacPherson, *Report on Insanity,* p. 603, footnote.

13. *Royal Commission,* p. 592 (data apply to Bengal Infantry).

14. Bg Jud D, 25-4-1806.

15. Md Mil L, 18-2-1794.

16. Md Mil B to Govt, 16-7-1844. Md Jud L, 3-1-1845. Md Mil B to G-i-C, 28-8-1846.

17. Bg Med B to Govt, 20-10-1847.

18. Bg Med B to Govt, 10-3-1851.

19. Acc Gen to Bg Govt, 21-3-1850.

20. Bg Accountant Gen to Govt, 21-3-1850.

21. Further Minute Govr Falkland, Bombay, 2-11-1849.

22. E. Eden, *Up the Country* (London and Dublin: Curzon, 1978 [1866]), pp. 36, 41, 59, 84.

23. Asy Sup to Bm Govt, 20-2-1850.

24. G. Aberigh-Mackay, *Twenty-one Days in India. Being the Tour of Sir Ali Baba, K.C.B.* (London: Thacker, 1902 [1880]), p. 184f.

25. Madras Citizens to Govt, 28-11-1851.

26. Bm Med B to Govt, 3-9-1853.

27. T.H. Thornton and J.L. Kipling, *Lahore* (Lahore: Govt Civil Secretariat Press, 1876). H.R. Goulding, *Old Lahore. Reminiscence of a Resident* (Lahore: Universal Books, 197– [1924]).

28. MacPherson, *Report on Insanity,* p. 605.

29. H.C. Burdett, *Hospitals and Asylums of the World: Their Origin, History, Construction, Administration, Management, and Legislation* (London: Churchill, 1891–3 (3 vols)), vol. 2 (1902), p. 62.

30. Asy Sup to Bm Med B, 28-2-1850.

31. Bm Asy Report, 31-3-1852.

32. Asy Sup to Bm Med B, 28-2-1850.

33. There prevailed prejudice towards southern-European people, as indicated by the failure to designate 'Portuguese' as 'European'. The concepts of 'nation-state', 'citizenship', and 'nationality' were also not yet concisely circumscribed. See also V.G. Kiernan, *The Lords of Human Kind. European Attitudes to the Outside World in the Imperial Age* (Harmondsworth: Penguin, 1972 [1969]), p. 29.

34. Asy Sup to Bm Med B, 28-2-1850.

35. Suptdg Surgeon Presidency to Md Med B, 23-1-1846.

36. Asy Sup to Suptdg Surg, Md Presidency, 15-7-1846.

37. Md Med B to Govt, 23-7-1846.

38. Md Mil B to G-i-C, 28-8-1846.

39. Md Mil Proc, 29-9-1846.

40. Bg Med B to Govt, 20-10-1847.

41. Bg Med B to Govt, 1-7-1820.

42. Munro to his sister, 1795, quoted in E. Stokes, *The English Utilitarians and India* (Delhi: Oxford University Press, 1982 [1959]), p. 25.

43. Elphinstone to Select Committee on Indian Affairs, 1832, cf. Stokes, *English Utilitarians,* p. 25.

44. Bg Asy Report, 14-6-1856.

45. Bg Asy Report, 14-6-1856.
46. Bg Asy Report, 14-6-1856.
47. Bg Med B to Govt, 1856.
48. Bg Asy Report, 14-6-1856.
49. Bg Med B to Govt, 31-5-1836.
50. Bg Asy Report, 14-6-1856.
51. Bg Hosp B to Govt, 26-1-1789.
52. Bm Med B to Govt, 18-3-1801.
53. M. Foucault, quoted in P. Sedgwick, *Psycho Politics* (London: Pluto, 1982), p 133.
54. Bg Asy Report, 14-6-1856.
55. Chief Mag and Supt Police to Md Mil B, 21-8-1852.
56. Bm Asy Report, 31-3-1852.
57. Nowadays mental 'disability' or 'feeblemindedness' is referred to as 'mental retardation', 'mental deficiency', and 'mental subnormality'. In line with present authoritative WHO definitions it is determined in relation to IQ scales, whereby a mental level below a certain standard (usually an IQ of seventy) is taken as deserving the label 'feeblemindedness'.

In accordance with Doerner and Plog the term 'mental disability' is seen as more appropriate for today's usage. The underlying assumption is that a person is disabled only in respect to their specific social situation and their age – not in an absolute or 'objective' sense. Somebody is mentally disabled only in respect to the expectations, demands, values, and norms of a specific environment.
K. Doerner and U. Plog, *Irren ist menschlich, oder: Lehrbuch der Psychiatrie/Psychotherapie* (Rehburg-Loccum: Psychiatrie-Verlag, 1980 [1978]).
58. Asy Supt to Bm Med B, 28-2-1850.
59. Asy Supt to Bm Med B, 28-2-1850.
60. Asy Supt to Bm Med B, 28-2-1850.
61. Asy Supt to Bm Med B, 28-2-1850.
62. Bm Asy Report, 31-3-1852.
63. Bm Asy Report, 31-3-1852.
64. W. Ernst and D. Kantowsky, 'Mad Tales from the Raj. Case Studies from Pembroke House and Ealing Lunatic Asylum, 1818–1892', in *Transaction/SOCIETY*, 3, 1985, pp. 31–8.
65. Bg Med B to Govt, 20-10-1847.
66. Bg Pub D, 28-6-1820.
67. Bg Med B to Govt, 5-2-1821.
68. Bg Asy Report, 14-6-1856.
69. Bg Asy Report, 14-6-1856.
70. Bg Asy Report, 14-6-1856.
71. Bg Med B to Govt, 31-5-1836.
72. Asy Sup to Bg Med B, 9-4-1856.
73. Bg Med B to Govt, 4-5-1836. Bg Med B to Govt, 7-5-1836.
74. Bg Asy Report, 14-6-1856.
75. Bg Asy Report, 14-6-1856.
76. Bg Asy Report, 14-6-1856.
77. S. Milligan, cf. C. Allen, *Plain Tales from the Raj. Images of British*

India in the twentieth century (London: Macdonald Futura, 1981 [1975]), p. 148.

78. See for details on medical treatment Chapter 5.

79. P. Spear, *The Nabobs. A Study of the Social Life of the English in eighteenth-century India* (London and Dublin: Curzon, 1980 [1932]), p. 3.

80. W. Ll. Parry-Jones, *The Trade in Lunacy. A Study of Private Madhouses in England in the eighteenth and nineteenth Centuries* (London: Routledge & Kegan Paul, 1972), pp. 329, 324, 327.

81. Summary of Correspondence relative to the Calcutta Asylum for Insane Persons, Undersec to Bg Govt, 30-12-1847.

82. Note by Sec to Bg Govt, 9-6-1852.

83. Bg Med B to Govt, 20-10-1847. Note, Accountant's Office, n.d. (1851?).

84. *Summary of Correspondence*, 30-12-1847.

85. Bg Med B to Govt, 27-3-1851.

86. Note by Sec to Bg Govt, 9-6-1852.

87. Parry-Jones, *Trade in Lunacy*, p. 200f.

88. Note by Sec to Bg Govt, 9-6-1852. Bg Med B to Govt, 10-3-1851.

89. Bg Med B to Govt, 10-3-1851.

90. Parry-Jones, *Trade in Lunacy*, p. 212ff.

91. Bg Jud D, 4-2-1852.

92. *Summary of Correspondence*, 30-12-1847.

93. Bm Asy Report, 31-3-1852.

3 The medical profession

1. W.Ll. Parry-Jones, *The Trade in Lunacy* (London: Routledge & Kegan Paul, 1972), p. 84.

2. A. Halliday, *A General View of the Present State of Lunatics, and Lunatic Asylums, in Great Britain and Ireland, and in some other Kingdoms* (London: Underwood, 1827), p. 7.

3. J. Conolly, 1830, quoted in Parry-Jones, *Trade in Lunacy*, p. 84.

4. J.M. Granville, 1877, quoted in A.T. Scull, *Museums of Madness* (Harmondsworth: Penguin Books, 1982 [1979]), p. 166.

5. W.B. Beatson, 'The Indian Medical Service, Past and Present', review in *British Medical Journal,* 2, 1902, p. 1182.

6. D. MacDonald, *Surgeons Twoe and a Barber. Being some Account of the Life and Work of the Indian Medical Service (1600–1947)* (London: Heinemann, 1950), p. 90.

7. MacDonald, *Surgeons Twoe*, p. 11.

8. MacDonald, *Surgeons Twoe*, p. 86ff.

9. D. MacDonald, 'The Indian Medical Service. A short account of its achievements. 1600–1947', in *Proceedings of the Royal Society of Medicine,* 49, 1956, p. 15.

10. MacDonald, *Surgeons Twoe*, p. 86.

11. MacDonald, *Surgeons Twoe*, p. 90.

12. Md Mil D, 20-8-1823.

13. F. Winslow, 1858; quoted in Parry-Jones, *Trade in Lunacy*, p. 88.

14. J. Conolly, 1830; quoted in Parry-Jones, *Trade in Lunacy*, p. 84.
15. Bg Med B to Govt, 31-5-1836.
16. Reference of Ass Surg Adam, 5-3-1821.
17. Quoted in Beardsmore to Bg Govt, 5-5-1836.
18. Bg Med B to Govt, 1-7-1820.
19. J. Sawers to Bg Med, 25-7-1820.
20. MacDonald, *Surgeons Twoe*, p. 109.
21. In 1790 the first Medical Society was founded in Bombay. Not much is known about its members' activities and it can be assumed that its professional leverage was not very great. This slowly changed with the establishment of the Medical and Physical Society of Bombay (1838), which became particulary renowned for its *Transactions*. In 1845 the Grant Medical College was opened. Finally, the Bombay branch of the British Medical Association was established in 1889. See D.G. Crawford, *A History of the Indian Medical Service, 1600–1913* (London: Thacker, 1914), vol. 2, pp. 454–5.
22. In 1855 aspirants to the medical service were required to have a command of surgery, of medicine, 'including the diseases of women and children, therapeutics, pharmacy, and hygiene', of anatomy and physiology, and of natural history, including botany and zoology. MacDonald, *Surgeons Twoe*, p. 109ff.
23. M'Cosh, *Medical Advice to the Indian Stranger* (London: W.H. Allen & Co, 1841), p. 20.
24. M'Cosh, *Medical Advice*, p. 42.
25. M'Cosh, *Medical Advice*, p. 20.
26. J.C. Bucknill and D.H. Tuke, 1858; J. M. Granville, 1877; cf. Scull, *Museums of Madness*, p. 166.
27. W.F. Bynum, 'Rationales for therapy in British psychiatry, 1780–1835', in *Medical History*, 18, 1974, p. 323.
28. G. Higgins, 1816, cf. Scull, *Museums of Madness*, p. 140.
29. T. Monro, 1815, cf. Scull, *Museums of Madness*, p. 137.
30. Bynum, *Rationales*, p. 325.
31. W. Battie, 1758, quoted in R. Porter, 'The history of institutional psychiatry in Europe', unpublished typescript.
32. Bg Med B to Govt, 20-10-1847.
33. Bg Med B to Govt, 2-4-1855.
34. M'Cosh, *Medical Advice*, p. 5.
35. M'Cosh, *Medical Advice*, p. 12.
36. M'Cosh, *Medical Advice*, p. 6.
37. M'Cosh, *Medical Advice*, p. 12.
38. Bm Mil D, 1826.
39. L.D. Smith, 'Behind Closed Doors; Lunatic Asylum Keepers, 1800–60', in *Social History of Medicine*, 1 (3), 1988, p. 309.
40. A.T. Scull, 'Mad-Doctors and Magistrates: English Psychiatry's Struggle for Professional Autonomy in the Nineteenth Century', in *European Journal of Sociology*, 17, 1976, pp. 279–305.
41. J. Conolly, 1856; quoted in Smith, *Behind Closed Doors*, p. 302.
42. D. Arnold, 'Medical Priorities and Practices in nineteenth-century British India', in *South Asia Research*, 5, 1985, p. 168.
43. M'Cosh, *Medical Advice*, p. 32.

44. M'Cosh, *Medical Advice*, p. 32.

45. Mrs R. Montgomery, Kanpur (Cambridge: Centre of South Asian Studies), 7-6-1931.

46. *Royal Commission on the Sanitary State of the Army in India* (London: Eyre and Spottiswoode for HMSO, 1863), p. XV.

47. J.R. Martin, 1835, quoted in Arnold, *Medical Priorities*, p. 9.

48. *Royal Commission*, p. XV.

49. D. Arnold, 'Cholera and Colonialism in British India', in *Past and Present*, 113, 1986, p. 127.

50. *Royal Commission*, p. XVII.

51. *Royal Commission*, p. XXX.

4 The patients

1. *Records of Pembroke House and Ealing Lunatic Asylum* (London: India Office Library and Records), Medical Certificates, 1845. Medical history of E.C. Zouch, 13-12-1844.

2. *Pembroke House*, Med Cert, 1845; Medical history of E.C. Zouch by Ass Surg J.F. Morier, 9-12-1844.

3. *Pembroke House*, Med Cert, 1843; case of Private T. Crawley.

4. *Pembroke House*, Med Cert, 1843; case of Gunner P. Lane.

5. *Pembroke House*, Med Cert, 1843; case of Private J. Brady.

6. *Pembroke House*, Med Cert, 1843; case of Gunner T. Hanlon.

7. Charge of E.C. Zouch by Sup Indian Navy, Bombay, 9-11-1839.

8. Records of Service for Indian Navy Officers, 1838–48; E.C. Zouch.

9. Sec to Govt, Bombay, 1-1-1840.

10. *Pembroke House*, Med Cert, 1846; case of Gunner D. Bell.

11. *Pembroke House*, Med Cert, 1843; case of Private W. Wooley.

12. *Pembroke House*, Med Cert, 1843; case of Lieutenant J.H. Hardisty.

13. Whitehall to India Board, 22-11-1856.

14. Certificate of Dr French, Haileybury, 16-6-1855.

15. Court of Directors to Board of Control, 7-8-1856.

16. J.W.J. Ouseley to India House, 31-8-1855.

17. Certificate of Sir R. Martin, 21-6-1855.

18. Whitehall to India Board, 22-11-1856.

19. India House to Ouseley, 7-5-1857.

20. Address by E.C. Zouch to Court, Bombay, 1839.

21. Bm Asy Report, 31-3-1852, Appendix.

22. Md Asy Report, 14-3-1808.

23. Bg Med B to Govt, 20-10-1847.

24. *Royal Commission on the Sanitary State of the Army in India* (London: Eyre and Spottiswoode for HMSO, 1863), vol. 1, p. XXIV.

25. Beardsmore to Bg Govt, 23-8-1820.

26. Md Med B to Govt, 15-2-1808.

27. *Pembroke House*, Med Cert, 1843; case of J. Kiernan.

28. E.J. Hobsbawm, *Industry and Empire* (Harmondsworth: Penguin Books, 1981 [1968]), p. 94.

29. *Pembroke House*, Med Cert, 1843; case of J. Kiernan.

30. *The East India Register and Army List* (London: Allen), February 1819.

31. Bg Med B to Govt, 10-3-1851.

32. Bg Asy Report, 14-6-1856; Summary of correspondence relative to the Calcutta Asylum for Insane Persons, Undersec to Bg Govt, 30-12-1847; Annual Return of Patients treated in the Asylum for European Insanes at Bhowanipore during the year 1859, 1-1-1860.

33. *Pembroke House*, Med Cert, 1853; case of F. Harvey.

34. *Pembroke House*, Med Cert, 1845; case of F.P. Thorne.

35. *Pembroke House*, Med Cert, 1845; case of E.C. Zouch.

36. *Pembroke House*, Med Cert, 1843; case of J. Tremlett.

37. *Royal Commission*, p. 755.

38. *Royal Commission*, p. 592.

39. Bm Asy Report, 31-3-1852.

5 Medical theory and practice

1. W.F. Bynum, 'Psychiatry in its historical context', in M. Shepherd and O.L. Zangwill, *Handbook of Psychiatry* (Cambridge: Cambridge University Press, 1982), vol. 1, p. 24.

2. R. Porter, 'Was there a moral therapy in eighteenth century psychiatry?', in *Lynchnos*, nn, 1981–2, pp. 12–26. R. Porter, 'In the eighteenth century were lunatic asylums total institutions?', in *Ego: Bulletin of the Department of Psychiatry, Guy's Hospital*, 4, 1983, pp. 12–34.

3. J. Locke, 'An essay concerning humane understanding' (1690), in R. Hunter and I. Macalpine, *Three Hundred Years of Psychiatry, 1535–1850: A History presented in selected English Texts* (London: Oxford University Press, 1963), p. 237.

4. R. Porter, 'Being Mad in Georgian England', *History Today*, 31, 1981, pp. 42–48.

5. Bg Med B to Govt, 30-11-1818.

6. Bm Med B to Govt, 24-5-1853.

7. Bynum, *Psychiatry in its historical context*, p. 26.

8. *Records of Pembroke House and Ealing Lunatic Asylums* (London: India Office Library and Records), Medical Certificates, 1854; case of Private G. Tracey.

9. Asy Sup to Bm Med B, 28-2-1851.

10. *Memorandum on the Census of British India of 1871–72* (London: Eyre and Spottiswoode, 1875), p. 37.

11. See for example Skultans who is actually an anthropologist and usually more sensitive towards various social groups' cosmologies. V. Skultans, *Madness and Morals. Ideas on Insanity in the Nineteenth Century* (London: Routledge and Kegan Paul, 1975), p. 2.

12. Asy Sup to Bg Govt, 14-6-1856.

13. J. MacPherson, 'Report on Insanity among Europeans in Bengal, founded on the experience of the Calcutta Lunatic Asylum', review in *Calcutta Review*, 26, 1856, p. 593.

14. Bg Med B to Govt, 30-11-1818.

15. D. MacPherson, quoting R. Martin, in *Royal Commission on the Sanitary State of the Army in India* (London: Eyre and Spottiswoode for HMSO, 1863), vol. 2, Appendix, p. 640. R. Martin, in *Royal Commission*, vol. 1, p. 10 (PS).

16. R. Martin, in *Royal Commission*, vol. 1, p. 10 (PS).

17. Bg Med B to Govt, 20-10-1847.

18. W.A. Green, 'Contributions towards the pathology of Insanity in India', in *The Indian Annals of Medical Science or half-yearly journal on practical medicine and surgery*, 4, 1857, pp. 374–435.

19. Green, *Contributions*, p. 376.

20. Sup Bhowanipur and Dhalanda Lun Asy to Med Dep, Bengal, 8-5-1858.

21. Green, *Contributions*, p. 375.

22. Sup Bhowanipur and Dhalanda Lun Asy to Med Dep, Bengal, 8-5-1858.

23. L.J. Ray, 'Models of Madness in Victorian Asylum Practice', in *European Journal of Sociology*, 22, 1981, pp. 229–63.

24. Maudsley quoting Bucknill, in Skultans, *Madness and Morals*, p. 6.

25. K. Ballhatchet, *Race, Sex and Class under the Raj. Imperial Attitudes and Policies and their Critics, 1793–1905* (London: Weidenfeld and Nicolson, 1980), p. 7.

26. Ray, *Models of Madness*.

27. Sup Bhowanipur and Dhalanda Lunatic Asy to Med Dep, Bengal, 8-5-1858.

28. Asy Sup to Bm Govt, 31-3-1852.

29. Asy Sup to Bm Govt, 31-3-1849.

30. *Pembroke House*, Med Cert, 1818–1892.

31. Editorial preface to *Transactions of the Medical and Physical Society Bombay*, 1, 1838, pp. IX–X.

32. *Pembroke House*, Med Cert, 1860; case of able seaman Charles Curtis.

33. Md Med B to Govt, 8-1-1820. Md Med B to Govt, 29-3-1802.

34. Md Med B to Govt, 8-1-1820.

35. Md Med B to Govt, 8-1-1820.

36. *Pembroke House*, Med Cert, 1860; case of able seaman Charles Curtis, case report, surgeon general hospital Calcutta, no date.

37. *Pembroke House*, Med Cert, Charles Curtis.

38. *Pembroke House*, Med Cert, Charles Curtis.

39. *Pembroke House*, Med Cert, Charles Curtis; Continuation of case report, Sup of Bhowanipur Asy, 15-2-1860.

40. *Pembroke House*, Med Cert, Charles Curtis; Continuation of case report.

41. *Pembroke House*, Med Cert, Charles Curtis; Continuation of case report.

42. See the title of G. Hill's 'Lecture': R.G. Hill, 'Total abolition of personal restraint in the treatment of the insane. A lecture on the management of lunatic asylums, and the treatment of the insane; delivered at the Mechanics' Institution, Lincoln, on the 21st of June, 1838, etc', in Hunter and Macalpine, *Three Hundred Years*, p. 886.

43. Hill, *Total abolition*, p. 892.

44. Asy Sup to Dir Gen Med Dep, Bengal, 8-5-1858.

45. Asy Sup to Dir Gen Med Dep, Bengal, 8-5-1858.

46. Asy Sup to Dir Gen Med Dep, Bengal, 8-5-1858.

47. Asy Sup to Dir Gen Med Dep, Bengal, 8-5-1858.

48. Asy Sup to Dir Gen Med Dep, Bengal, 8-5-1858.

49. Asy Sup to Dir Gen Med Dep, Bengal, 8-5-1858.

50. Asy Sup to Dir Gen Med Dep, Bengal, 8-5-1858.

51. Asy Sup to Dir Gen Med Dep, Bengal, 8-5-1858.

52. Minute by Second Member of Med B, Madras, 4-3-1808.

53. J. Reid, 1808, quoted in R. Porter, 'The History of Institutional Psychiatry in Europe', unpublished typescript.

54. Bentinck to Metcalfe, 16-9-1829, and to Mancy, 1-6-1834; quoted in P. Spear, *The Oxford History of Modern India, 1740–1975* (Delhi: Oxford University Press, 1984 [1965]), p. 145.

55. Green, *Contributions*, pp. 374–5.

56. Green, *Contributions*, pp. 375–6.

57. J.R. Miller, MD, Surgeon, 'Annual Report of the 23rd Regt Native Light Infantry', in *Transactions of the Medical and Physical Society, Bombay*, 4, 1857–8, p. 274.

58. Macpherson, *Report on Insanity*, p. 598.

59. F.S. Arnott, MD, Surgeon 'Report on the Health of the 1st Bombay European Regiment', in *Transactions of the Medical and Physical Society of Bombay*, 2, 1855, p. 157.

60. A.S. Thomson, MD, 'Could the Natives of a temperate climate colonize and increase in a tropical country and vice versa?', in *Transactions of the Medical and Physical Society of Bombay*, 6, 1843, pp. 112–37.

61. Thomson, *Natives of a temperate climate*, pp. 112–37. See also D. Arnold, 'White Colonization and Labour in nineteenth-century India', in *Journal of Imperial and Commonwealth History*, 2, 1983, pp. 133–58.

62. Thomson, *Natives of a temperate climate*, p. 113.

63. Thomson, *Natives of a temperate climate*, p. 114–15.

64. Thomson, *Natives of a temperate climate*, p. 116.

65. *Pembroke House*, Med Cert, 1852; case of H. Strauch.

6 'Mad dogs and Englishmen . . . '

1. M. Foucault, *Folie et Déraison. Histoire de la folie à l'âge classique* (Paris: Librairie Plon, 1961), p. VII. In unison with his structuralist approach Foucault then goes on to claim: 'à défaut de cette inaccessible pureté primitive, l'étude structurale doit remonter vers la décision qui lie et sépare à la fois raison et folie; elle doit tendre à découvrir l'échange perpétuel, l'obscure racine commune, l'affrontement originaire qui donne sens à l'unité aussi bien qu'à l'opposition du sens et de l'insensé'. This position of Foucault is not fully shared by the author.

2. Report Bm Lun Asy, 31-3-1852.

3. K. Ballhatchet, *Race, Sex and Class under the Raj. Imperial Attitudes and Policies and their Critics, 1793–1905* (London: Weidenfeld and Nicolson, 1980), p. 3.

4. G. Balandier, 1951, quoted in D. Frigessi Castelnuovo and M. Risso, *Emigration und Nostalgie. Sozialgeschichte, Theorie und Mythos psychischer Krankheit von Auswanderern* (Frankfurt am Main: Cooperative-Verlag, 1986), p. 145. (orig. edn: *A mezza parete. Emigrazione, nostalgia, malattia mentale* (Torino: Giulio Einaudi editore, 1982).

Index